TALES FOR TELLING

TALES FOR TELLING

By

Katherine Williams Watson

Formerly Head Children's Department,
Denver Public Library

NEW YORK
THE H. W. WILSON COMPANY
1950

Preface

Most of the stories included in this collection were found in old volumes of magazines, particularly *St. Nicholas,* and in books which are now out of copyright. Among the selections the reader will find many of his old favorites in condensed form and others that will be new to him. "The Kingdom of the Greedy" is a fine story, but not used by many story-tellers because of its length, so it has been condensed for radio time; much of the description could be eliminated without injuring the story. In general, the magazine stories required more extensive editing than those published in books. Only trifling changes in wording have been made in the stories translated from the Norse by Sir George W. Dasent and in Howard Pyle's tales, while Andersen's "Loveliest Rose in the World" has such a delightful form that it didn't seem advisable to change a word.

The following acknowledgments are made with thanks to those who have courteously given permission for the use of copyright material in this book:

Robert L. Grimes for "The Baker's Top-hat Bunny," which appeared in *Jack and Jill Magazine.*

Miss Toni Hult for "The Left-Handed Christmas," which appeared in *Adventure Trails for Boys and Girls.*

Thomas Nelson & Sons for "Tamlane," reprinted from *Fairies and Enchanters,* by Amabel Williams-Ellis, copyright 1934 by Thomas Nelson & Sons.

All stories in this volume may be used on non-commercial broadcasts without payment of royalty. With the two exceptions noted below, permission to use these stories on commercial broadcasts must be obtained in writing from the H. W. Wilson Company. Permission to use "Tamlane" on commercial broadcasts must be secured from

Thomas Nelson & Sons and permission to use "The Marvel of the Sword" on commercial broadcasts must be secured from the J. B. Lippincott Company.

June 1950

KATHERINE WILLIAMS WATSON

CONTENTS

A Note on Radio Story Telling

I have often been asked to give a few pointers on radio story telling for children. An identifying phrase or poem is a valuable addition at the start of a children's program. Even today after being off the air for several years I still meet people who remember our radio program on station KOA, Denver, by the familiar phrase we used at the beginning of the story which was

> "Anything can happen,
> In fairy tale or rhyme
> Beginning with the magic words
> *Once upon a time.*"

Some of the better broadcasts are prepared by storytellers in collaboration with the professional script-writers of the broadcasting staff. This was especially true when we put on children's plays, like those to be found in my *Radio Plays for Children* (Wilson). Radio story telling should be given in an easy conversational style, in simple language and with enthusiasm. The dial is readily turned away from stories which are uninteresting or poorly delivered.

The person who tells stories on the radio must first be fully prepared. Six typewritten sheets, double spaced, will take fifteen minutes to read at the ordinary speed of conversation. Use soft paper in order to avoid rattling sounds when the sheets are turned. Practice in timing is very important, so that one will not be hurried on the last page. I usually allowed an extra minute, but this was only my way in telling stories, and would probably not apply to others. It is wise to allow a few minutes alone before the broadcast begins, to catch your breath, and to get your papers in order.

9

Stories must have the sparkle, the lively action, the not too descriptive passage, the surprise developments that make them come true in the voice of the radio story-teller. Most important of all they should have literary merit. For little children they should be fairly short. Children will not listen if they are bored. The average reading time for older children is fifteen minutes. One should have a low-pitched voice. This can be cultivated, for my radio voice is much lower than my speaking voice. It is important to use familiar words, short sentences, simple vocabulary, good diction and clear enunciation. Stories should also be read in a conversational manner. Mannerisms must be avoided. Read your story aloud several times, and above all things be natural, by being yourself. Insincerity and affectation are more noticeable over the radio than almost anywhere else. The microphone emphasizes nasal and shrill tones. Since it is a very delicate instrument, it is important not to speak with the mouth too close to the mouthpiece. And don't talk too fast! How often one hears radio material read too fast. Pauses are important.

In my story telling I would try to see into the homes of the children where my voice would penetrate. Perhaps this mental picture of the children in the far scattered ranches of our western country helped to keep the program on the air seven happy years.

K. W. W.

Christmas

The Cat's Christmas

From *The New Year's Bargain*, by Susan Coolidge.

7 minutes

High up in the church steeple the bells were ringing the Christmas chimes. The wind blew and clouds drifted rapidly over the face of the moon. Frost glittered on the roofs. The watchman on his rounds clapped his hands and stamped his feet to keep himself warm. A homeless cat crouched beneath the window and shivered in the cold. She heard the watchman cry out, "Eight o'clock, and all's well."

But to the poor cat all was not well. She heard the bells in the tower ring out their sweet tones. They seemed to say, "Peace on earth, good will to men!" "Alas," sighed the cat, "this does not mean good will to me. Poor me! Whew! what a wind! Where shall I go?"

Overcome by her sorrows the cat gave a loud wail, which rang out in the chilly air. High and low did she search—over the fence, under the vine—but no shelter could be found. The vine was leafless and the fence gave no hiding place. At last she remembered the kitchen roof. She could easily mount it by the rain trough. Perhaps there might be a warm chimney there—no bad pillow on this wintry night!

Sure enough the chimney was warm and, curling in a ball, Puss laid herself to rest against it. Perhaps it was not warm enough, or perhaps she could not forget her sorrows, but certain it is she could not sleep. She wriggled, she twisted; she sent forth melancholy cries. Nine—ten—eleven had sounded before she had fallen into her first doze.

The clock was on the stroke of twelve, when a scraping sound close by roused her. Was it some other cat, or a big rat from the cellar, scaling the wall? Raising herself, she listened.

13

No, it was neither cat nor rat. Light hoofs were climbing the tiles. Bells tinkled and a small sleigh drawn by reindeer came into view. Swift as light it flew over the roof and then paused at the chimney. Quickly a little old man jumped out. His jolly face shone in the moonlight like a red apple. His fat, plump body was wrapped in fur, and on his back he carried a bag.

Puss had never seen the old man before, but she knew him well. It was the good St. Nicholas! Down the chimney he went with a motion like a bird's; up again as fast. Then he searched in his bag and his kind face looked puzzled. The cat sprang forward, and rubbed her soft fur against his legs.

"Well, Puss," said the saint, "how come you're out on the roof this cold, wintry night? What can I do for you? Wish a wish, if you have one. I'm in a humor for pleasing everybody, while I'm about it."

So the cat told her story. "And for a wish," she said, "if your saintship would only permit me to slip into your sleigh, under your furs, I should be proud and happy. They look warm and comfortable. I take very little room," she added piteously.

"Is that all? Jump in at once," said kind St. Nicholas. "My sleigh is never full. There's room for forty cats like you. Ho! Ho!" and he laughed a jolly laugh. So pussy sprang into the sleigh and off they went.

St. Nicholas and the cat flew from roof to roof. In the magic stillness of their flight no sound was heard but the soft tinkling of sleigh bells. First to one chimney, then to another; bag after bag full of toys and candies; here a doll, there a drum or sled. Sometimes warm stockings and little shoes were left in the homes they visited. Everybody was given something from the wonderful bag.

To stately places, to cellars and lonely attics; at last to a church, dim and fragrant with ivy leaves and twisted evergreen, where their errand was to feed a hungry robin

14

who had found shelter there. How his beads of eyes sparkled as the saint awoke him! How eagerly he pecked the red berries which were his Christmas gift, though he had hung up no stocking.

To small, to great, to rich and to poor alike, the good saint had an errand. Little ones smiled in their sleep as he moved by, and birds twittered and chirped. Bells faintly tinkled and chimed as in a dream. Flying fairies made room for the sleigh to pass and the world received a blessing as it slept—a Christmas blessing.

Through the air, more towns, more villages. Now the sea was below them, the cold, moonlit sea. Island after island came into view, but the sleigh did not stop. Then again land came in sight, towers and steeples, big houses, and little huts, homes of the rich and homes of the poor.

A wild desire seized the cat. She begged St. Nicholas to take her down a wide chimney on his shoulder. She longed to see the good saint at his kind work. Down they went into a pretty room, where sleeping children lay in their little beds. Stockings were hung up by the fireplace. Out of the bag came beautiful presents for these little ones.

Up to the roof and into the sleigh again. The cat sighed softly as she crept under the fur robe. But St. Nicholas chuckled as he shook the reins and urged on his frisky reindeer. "I see what the cat wants," he murmured. "A home shall be her Christmas gift."

At last they came to a small house with a roof so poor and low that only a saint would have noticed the little chimney in the darkness. No stockings hung by the cold fireplace, but in a poor little bed a pale-faced boy lay sleeping.

"I wonder," thought Puss, "what gift he will leave here." The saint's eyes twinkled as he said, "You need a home; this little fellow wants a playmate, so you shall be his Christmas gift."

And with a "Merry Christmas," he sprang up the chimney and was gone. Whither he went the cat knew not; for where St. Nicholas hides himself during the year is one of the secrets that no one knows.

The Christmas Masquerade

From *The Pot of Gold,* by Mary E. Wilkins Freeman.   15 minutes

On Christmas Eve the Mayor's mansion presented a beautiful appearance. The Mayor was giving a Christmas masquerade to all the children in the city, the poor as well as the rich. Placards had been put up in the most conspicuous places in the town, and all the daily papers had at least a column devoted to it, headed with the MAYOR'S CHRISTMAS MASQUERADE in large letters.

It was to be a children's ball, and they were to select their own costumes. The Mayor had promised to pay the expenses of all the poor children whose parents were unable to do so, and the bills for their costumes were to be sent to him.

Of course there was a great deal of excitement among the regular costumers of the city. But the placards and the notices had not been out a week before a new costumer appeared, who cast all the others into the shade. He set up his shop on the corner of one of the principal streets, and hung up his beautiful costumes in the windows. He was a little fellow, not much larger than a boy of ten. His cheeks were as red as roses, and he had on a long curling wig as white as snow. He wore a suit of crimson velvet knee breeches and a little swallow-tailed coat with beautiful golden buttons. Deep lace ruffles fell over his slender white hands, and he wore elegant knee buckles of glittering stones.

It did not take the children long to discover what beautiful things he had, and how superior he was to the other costumers, and they began to flock to his shop immediately,

17

from the Mayor's daughter to the poor rag-picker's. Some of the children decided to be fairies, others shepherdesses, and still others princesses, according to their own fancies, and the new costumer had charming costumes to suit them.

At last Christmas Eve came, and the children flocked into the Mayor's own mansion. His daughter, who had chosen the character of a goose-girl, looked so real that one could hardly believe she was anything else. And so it was with all the others—the Red Ridinghoods, the Princesses, the Bopeeps, and all the rest who came to the Mayor's ball. What fun they did have! The fiddlers fiddled, and the children danced on the beautiful waxed floors. The supper was served at midnight—and such a supper! There were mountains of pink and white ices, and cakes with sugar castles. Under each child's plate there was a pretty present, and everyone had a basket of candy and cake to carry home.

At four o'clock the fiddlers put up their fiddles and the children went home: fairies, shepherdesses, pages, and princesses all saying what a splendid time they had had.

But in a short time what consternation there was throughout the city! When the proud and fond parents attempted to unbutton their children's dresses, to prepare them for bed, not a single costume would come off. The parents were dreadfully frightened. But the children were so tired out that their mothers finally let them go to bed in their fancy costumes, and thought perhaps they would come off better in the morning. So Red Ridinghood went to bed in her cloak, holding fast to her basket of dainties for her grandmother, and Bopeep slept with her crook in her hand.

All was quiet till noon, when the children woke up. Then a great wave of alarm spread over the city, for still not one of the costumes would come off. It was all so mysterious and dreadful. The news spread rapidly over the city, and soon a great crowd gathered around the new

18

costumer's shop, for everyone thought he must be responsible for all the mischief.

The shop door was locked, but they soon battered it down with stones. When they rushed in the costumer was not there; he had disappeared with all his wares. Then they did not know what to do, and they were getting desperate.

Finally, the Mayor called a meeting of the Aldermen, and they all assembled in the City Hall. Nearly every one of them had a child who was a chimney-sweep, or a little match-girl or a shepherdess. They appointed a chairman and took a great many votes, but they did not agree on anything, until some one proposed that they consult the Wise Woman, who lived all alone with her Black Cat in a little hut on the outskirts of town.

But when the Aldermen reached her house and found her sitting by the fire, holding her Black Cat, a new difficulty arose. She was so deaf that she could not distinguish a tone below G-sharp. The Aldermen screamed until they were red in the face, but to no purpose.

So they all went back home and decided to send the highest High Soprano Singer in the church choir to the Wise Woman, for she could sing up to G-sharp. She set out in the Mayor's coach, and the Aldermen marched behind, swinging their gold-headed canes.

The High Soprano Singer put her head down close to the Wise Woman's ear and sang in G-sharp all about the Christmas masquerade and the dreadful dilemma everybody was in, and the Wise Woman heard every word.

"Go home, and give 'em a spoonful of castor oil," she piped up; then she took a pinch of snuff and wouldn't say any more.

So the Aldermen went home, and each one took a district and marched through it with a servant carrying an immense bowl and spoon, and every child had to take a dose of castor oil. But it didn't do a bit of good. So the

19

Aldermen took the High Soprano Singer, and they consulted the Wise Woman again.

"Give 'em a spanking all 'round," the Wise Woman snapped out, "and if that don't work, put 'em to bed without their supper!"

Then the Aldermen marched back to try that; and all the children in the city were spanked and when that didn't do any good, they were put to bed without any supper. But the next morning, when they woke up, their costumes still would not come off.

So they set out for the Wise Woman's again, with the High Soprano Singer. She sang in G-sharp how the Aldermen and the Mayor considered the Wise Woman an imposter, and told her to take her Black Cat and move beyond the limits of the city.

"Deary me," piped the Wise Woman, when the singing was finished, "how very grand these gentlemen are!" Her Black Cat put up his back and spit.

"Five times one Black Cat are five Black Cats," said the Wise Woman. And directly, there were five Black Cats, spitting and miaowing.

"Five times five Black Cats are twenty-five Black Cats." And then there were twenty-five of the angry little beasts.

"Five times twenty-five Black Cats are one hundred and twenty-five Black Cats," added the Wise Woman, with a chuckle.

Then the Mayor and the Aldermen and the High Soprano Singer fled out the door and back to the city. One hundred and twenty-five Black Cats had seemed to fill the Wise Woman's hut full, and when they all spit and miaowed together, it was dreadful. The visitors could not wait for her to multiply Black Cats any longer.

As winter wore on and spring came, the condition of things grew worse. Physicians had been consulted, who advised that the children should be allowed to follow their own bents and act as they were dressed, for fear of injury to their constitutions. So the rich aldermen's daughters were actually out in the fields herding sheep, and their sons were sweeping chimneys, or carrying newspapers; while the poor charwomen's and coal-heaver's children spent their time like princesses and fairies. Such a topsy-turvy state of society was shocking. Why, the Mayor's little daughter was tending geese out in the meadow like any common goose-girl!

When cherries were ripe in spring, Violetta, the Mayor's older daughter thought she would ask the Cherry-man about it. So she told him all about the great trouble that had come upon the city. He listened in great astonishment; he lived several miles out in the country, and had not heard of it before.

"How did the costumer look?" he asked.

Then Violetta described the costumer and told him of the unavailing attempts that had been made to find him.

"I know where he is!" said the Cherry-man. "He's up in one of my cherry trees. He's been living there ever since the cherries were ripe, and he won't come down."

Then Violetta ran and told her father in great excitement, and he at once called a meeting of the Aldermen, and in a few hours half the city was on the road to the Cherry-man's.

He had a beautiful orchard of cherry trees, all laden with fruit. And, sure enough, in one of the largest, way up amongst the topmost branches, sat the costumer in his red velvet short-clothes and his diamond knee-buckles. He looked down through the green boughs. "Good morning, friends," he shouted.

The Aldermen shook their gold-headed canes at him, and the people danced round the tree in a rage. Then they tried to climb, but they soon found that to be impossible. As fast as they touched a hand or foot to the tree, back it flew with a jerk exactly as if the tree pushed it. They tried a ladder, but the ladder fell back the moment it touched the tree, and lay sprawling upon the ground. Finally, they brought axes and thought they could chop the tree down, costumer and all; but the wood resisted the axes as if it were iron, and only dented them, receiving no impression itself.

Meanwhile, the costumer sat up in the tree, eating cherries and throwing the stones down. Finally, he stood up on a stout branch, and looking down, addressed the people.

"It's of no use, your trying to accomplish anything in this way," he said; "I'm willing to come to terms with you, and make everything right, on two conditions."

The people grew quiet then, and the Mayor stepped forward as spokesman. "Name your two conditions," he said. "You own that you are the cause of all this trouble."

"Well," said the costumer, reaching out for a handful of cherries, "this Christmas masquerade of yours was a beautiful idea; but you wouldn't do it every year, and your successors might not do it at all. I want those poor children to have a Christmas every year. My first condition is, that every poor child in the city hangs its stocking for gifts in the City Hall on every Christmas Eve, and gets it filled, too. I want the resolution filed and put away in the city archives."

"We agree to the first condition!" cried the people with one voice, without waiting for the Mayor and Aldermen.

"The second condition," said the costumer, "is that this good young Cherry-man here have the Mayor's daughter, Violetta, for his wife. He has been kind to me, letting me live in his cherry tree, and eat his cherries, and I want to reward him."

"We consent!" cried all the people; but the Mayor, though he was so generous, was a proud man. "I will not consent to the second condition," he cried angrily.

"Very well," replied the costumer, picking some more cherries, "then your youngest daughter tends geese the rest of her life, that's all!"

The Mayor was in great distress; but the thought of his youngest daughter being a goose-girl all her life was too much for him and he gave in at last.

"Now go home, and take the costumes off your children," said the costumer, "and leave me in peace to eat cherries!"

Then the people hastened back to the city and found to their great delight that the costumes would come off. The children were soon dressed in their own proper clothes and were their own proper selves once more.

The princesses and the fairies put on their own suitable dresses and all the others went about their useful employments. There was great rejoicing in every home. Violetta thought she had never been so happy, now that her dear little sister was no longer a goose-girl.

The resolution to provide every poor child in the city with a stocking full of gifts on Christmas was solemnly filed, and deposited in the city archives, and was never broken.

Violetta was married to the Cherry-man, and all the children came to the wedding. The costumer had mysteriously disappeared from the cherry tree the night before, but he left some beautiful wedding presents for the bride under the tree—a silver service with a pattern of cherries engraved on it, a set of china with hand-painted cherries on it, and a white satin robe, embroidered with cherries down the front.

The Christmas Monks

From *The Pot of Gold,* by Mary E. Wilkins
Freeman.   18 minutes

All children have wondered where the Christmas presents come from. Where does Santa Claus get them? Well! the answer is—in the garden of the Christmas Monks.

The Convent of the Christmas Monks is a very charming place. The monks are a jolly brethren; the robes of their order are white, and they never are seen out at any time of the year without Christmas wreaths on their heads. Every morning they file in a long procession into the chapel, to sing a Christmas carol; and every evening they ring a Christmas chime on the convent bells.

But the principal thing about the Convent of the Christmas Monks is the garden; for that is where the Christmas presents grow. Every year they sow the Christmas present seeds, after they have ploughed the ground and made it ready.

There is one enormous bed devoted to rocking-horses. This seed is very curious; just little bits of rocking-horses so small that they can only be seen through a very, very powerful microscope. The monks drop these at quite a distance from each other, so that they will not interfere while growing; then they cover them up neatly with earth, and put up a signpost with "Rocking-horses" on it in evergreen letters. Just so with the penny trumpet seed, and the toy furniture seed, the skate seed, the sled seed, and all the others.

Perhaps the prettiest and most interesting part of the garden, is that devoted to wax dolls. There are other beds for the commoner dolls—for the rag dolls, and the china dolls. Wax dolls have to be planted quite early in the season; for they need a good start before the sun is very high. The seeds are the loveliest bits of tiny dolls imaginable. The monks sow them pretty close together, and they begin to come up by the middle of May. There is first just a little glimmer of gold, or black, or brown as the case may be, above the soil. Then the snowy foreheads appear, and the blue eyes, and black eyes, and, later on, all those enchanting little heads are out of the ground. Gradually, more and more of them come to light, and finally by Christmas they are all ready to gather. There they stand, swaying to and fro, their dresses of pink, or blue, or white—for their dresses grow with them—fluttering in the air. The bed of wax dolls in the garden of the Christmas monks is just about the prettiest sight in the world.

There was great excitement among the young folk of the countryside and older ones too, when one evening there appeared hung in a conspicuous place on the garden hedge, a broad strip of white cloth trimmed with evergreen and printed with the notice:

> "Wanted—by the Christmas Monks, two *good* boys to assist in garden work. Applicants will be examined by Fathers Anselmus and Ambrose, in the Convent refectory, on April 10th."

This notice was hung out about five o'clock in the evening, some time in the early part of February. There wasn't a boy in the country who wouldn't have liked this position. To work all the year in that wonderful garden, and see all those beautiful toys growing, was their greatest ambition.

But the great difficulty, of course, was about the degree of goodness necessary to pass the examination. When the time drew near, there were two boys whom every one thought would get the jobs, although some of the other boys had lingering hopes for themselves. Still all the older people had decided in their minds that the monks would choose these two boys. One was the Prince, the King's oldest son; and the other was a poor boy named Peter. The Prince was the biggest rogue in the whole country; but the lords and ladies said it was their solemn belief that the Prince was the best boy in the whole kingdom.

Peter was really and truly such a good boy that there was no excuse for saying he was not. His father and mother were poor people; and Peter worked every minute out of school hours, to help them along. Then he had a sweet little crippled sister whom he never tired of caring for, and he also found time to do many little kindnesses for other people. He always studied his lessons faithfully, and never ran away from school. Peter was such a good boy that everybody loved him.

When the examination day came all the boys from far and near, with their hair brushed and parted, and dressed in their best clothes, flocked into the convent. The two fathers who were to examine the boys were perched up in a high pulpit. Father Anselmus was a little the taller of the two; and Father Ambrose was a little the broader; and that was about all the difference between them in looks.

The little boys all stood up in a row, and the examination began. Many failed to pass because the fathers found out that this boy had robbed birds' nests, and that one had stolen apples. And one after another they walked disconsolately away until there were only two boys left: the Prince and Peter.

"Now, your Highness," said Father Anselmus to the Prince, "are you a good boy?"

"O Holy Father!" exclaimed all the people—there were a good many fine folks from the court present. "He is such a good boy! we never knew him to do a wrong thing."

"I don't suppose he ever robbed a bird's nest?" said Father Ambrose, a little doubtfully.

"No, no!" chorused the people.

At last everybody being so confident that there could be no reasonable fault found with the Prince, he was pronounced competent to enter upon the monks' service. Peter they knew a great deal about. So after a few questions, they accepted him also; and the people went home and left the two boys with the Christmas Monks.

The next morning Peter was obliged to lay aside his homespun coat, and the Prince his velvet tunic, and both were dressed in little white robes. Then the Prince was set to sowing Noah's Ark seed, and Peter picturebook seed. Up and down they went scattering the seed. Peter sang a little psalm to himself, but the Prince grumbled because they hadn't given him gold watch seed to plant instead of the toy he had outgrown long ago. By noon Peter had planted all the picturebooks, and fastened the card to mark them on a pole; but the Prince had dawdled so his work was not half done.

"We are going to have a trial with this boy," said the monks to each other, "we shall have to set him a penance at once, or we cannot manage him at all."

So the Prince had to go without his dinner, and kneel on dried peas in the chapel all the afternoon. The next day he finished his Noah's Ark meekly; but on the following day he rebelled again and had to go the whole length of the field where they planted jew's-harps, on his knees. And so it went, about every other day for the whole year. The Prince became dreadfully tired of his convent life. Peter, on the contrary, had never been so happy in his life. He worked like a bee, and enjoyed seeing all the lovely things he had planted, come up. Then too, he had never fared so well in his life. He could never remember the time before when he had been a whole week without being hungry. He sent his wages home to his parents; and he never ceased to wonder at the discontent of the Prince.

"They grow so slowly," the Prince would say, "I expected to have a bushelful of new toys every month. And the monks say I can only have my usual Christmas share anyway, nor can I pick them out myself. I never saw such a stupid place to stay in all my life." Peter tried to comfort him, but it was not of much use, for the Prince became angry because Peter was not discontented too.

Two weeks before Christmas everything in the garden was nearly ready to be picked. Some few things needed a little more December sun, but everything looked perfect. Some of the Jack-in-the-Boxes would not pop out quite quick enough, and some of the Jumping-Jacks were hardly as limber as they might have been; that was all. As it was so near Christmas the monks were engaged in their holy exercises in the chapel for the greater part of the time, and only went over the garden once a day to see if everything was all right.

One morning the Prince was at one end of the garden straightening up some wooden soldiers which had toppled over, and Peter was in the wax doll bed dusting the dolls. All of a sudden he heard a sweet little voice, "O, Peter." He thought at first one of the dolls was talking, but they couldn't say anything but papa and mama, so he looked around. "Here I am, Peter!" and there was a little pull at his sleeve. There was his little sister. She was not any taller than the dolls around her, and looked uncommonly like the prettiest, pinkest-cheeked, yellow-haired ones; so it was no wonder that Peter didn't see her at first. She stood there poising herself on her crutches, and smiling lovingly up at Peter.

"Oh, you darling!" cried Peter, catching her up in his arms. "How did you get in here?"

"I came in behind one of the monks," said she. "He was going up the street past our house, and I kept behind him all the way. When he opened the gate I whisked in too, and then I followed him into the garden. I've been here with the dollies ever since."

"Well," said Peter. "I don't see what I am going to do with you, now that you are here. I can't let you out again; and I don't know what the monks will say."

"Oh, I know!" cried the little girl gaily. "I'll stay out here in the garden. I can sleep in one of those beautiful doll cradles over there; and you can bring me something to eat."

"But the monks come out every morning to look over the garden, and they'll be sure to find you," said her brother, anxiously.

"No, I'll hide! Oh, Peter, here is a place where there isn't any doll."

"Yes, that doll didn't come up."

"Well, I'll tell you what I'll do. I'll just stand here in her place, and nobody can tell the difference."

"I don't know but you can," said Peter, although he was still ill at ease. He was so good that he didn't want to offend his friends the monks; at the same time he couldn't help being glad to see his little sister.

He smuggled some food out to her, and she played merrily about him all day; and at night he tucked her into one of the doll's cradles with lace pillows and quilt of rose-colored silk.

The next morning when the monks were going the rounds, the father who inspected the wax doll bed, was a bit nearsighted, and he never noticed the difference between the dolls and Peter's little sister, who looked just as much like a wax doll as she possibly could. So the two were delighted with the success of their plans.

Something else happened now; the Prince ran away. He had been watching a long time for an opportunity to possess himself of a certain long ladder, which the monks kept locked up in the toolhouse. Lately, by some oversight, the door had been left unlocked, and the Prince got the ladder. It was the latter part of the afternoon, and the Christmas monks were all in the chapel practicing Christmas carols. The Prince found a very large hamper, and packed as many Christmas presents for himself as he could stuff into it; then he put the ladder against the high gate in front of the convent, and climbed up, dragging the hamper after him. He gave his foot a little triumphant kick as he looked at his prison from the top, but he lost his balance. He screamed with all the force of his royal lungs; was heard by a party of noblemen who were galloping up the street; was rescued, and carried to the palace. But he was obliged to drop the hamper of presents when he fell.

When the good monks discovered the escape of the Prince, they were greatly grieved, and poor Peter could with difficulty be comforted. He had been very fond of the Prince, although the latter had done little except torment him the whole year; but Peter had a way of being fond of people.

A few days after the Prince ran away, and the day before the one on which the Christmas presents were to be gathered, the nearsighted father went out into the wax doll field again; but this time he had his glasses on, and could see just as well as any one, and even a little better. Peter's little sister was swinging herself on her crutches, in the place where the wax doll didn't come up, tipping her little face up, and smiling just like the dolls around her.

"Why, what is this!" said the father. I thought that wax doll didn't come up. Can my eyes deceive me? There is a doll there—and what a doll! on crutches, and in a poor, homely dress! It is a miracle!" exclaimed he. "The little girl is alive! I will pick her and take her to the brothers, and we will pay her the honors she is entitled to."

Then the good father picked up Peter's little sister, who was trembling in all her little bones, and carried her into the chapel, where the monks were just assembling to sing another carol. He went right up to the Christmas abbot.

"Most holy abbot," said the nearsighted father, holding out Peter's little sister, "behold a miracle. Thou wilt remember that there was one wax doll planted which did not come up. Behold, in her place I have found this doll on crutches, which is—alive!"

"Let me see her!" said the abbot. "Why, this is verily a miracle!"

The brother who was the leach of the convent, came forward. "Let me look at the miracle, most holy abbot," said he. He took up Peter's sister, and looked carefully at the small, twisted ankle. "I thing I can cure this with my herbs," he said.

"But I don't know," said the abbot doubtfully. "I never heard of curing a miracle."

"If it is not lawful, my humble power will not suffice to cure it," said the father.

"True," said the abbot. "Take her, then, and exercise thy healing art upon her, and we will go on with our Christmas devotions, for which we should now feel all the more zeal." So the father took away Peter's little sister, who was still too frightened to speak. The Christmas Monk was a wonderful doctor, for by Christmas Eve the little girl was completely cured of her lameness.

Peter of course heard the talk about the miracle, and knew at once what it meant. He was almost heartbroken to think he was deceiving the monks, but at the same time he did not dare to confess the truth for fear they would put a penance upon his sister, and he could not bear to think of her having to kneel upon dried peas.

He worked hard picking Christmas presents, and hid his unhappiness as best he could. On Christmas Eve he was called into the chapel. The Christmas Monks were all assembled there. The walls were covered with green garlands, and boughs and sprays of hollyberries with wax lights gleaming brightly amongst them. The altar and the picture of the Blessed Child behind it were so bright as to almost dazzle one; and right up in the midst of it, in a lovely white dress, all wreaths and jewels, in a little chair with a canopy of green branches over it, sat Peter's little sister.

And there were all the Christmas Monks in their white robes and wreaths, going up in a long procession, with their hands full of the very showiest Christmas presents to offer them to her! But when they reached her and held out the lovely presents—the first was an enchanting wax doll, the biggest beauty in the whole garden—instead of reaching out her hands for them, she just drew back, and said in her sweet little piping voice, "Please, I'm not a millacle, I'm only Peter's little sister."

"Peter?" said the abbot, "the Peter who works in our garden?"

"Yes," said the little sister.

Now here was a fine opportunity for a whole convent full of monks to look foolish—filing up in procession with their hands full of gifts to offer to a miracle, and finding there was no miracle, but only Peter's little sister.

But the abbot of the Christmas Monks had always maintained that there were two ways of looking at all things; if any object was not what you wanted it to be in one light, there was sure to be another light in which it would meet your views. So now he brought this philosophy to bear.

"This little girl did not come up in the place of the wax doll, and she is not a miracle in that light," said he, "but look at her in another light and she is a miracle—do you not see?"

They all looked at her, the darling little girl, the very meaning and sweetness of all Christmas in her loving, trusting, innocent face.

"Yes," said all the Christmas Monks, "she is a miracle." And they all laid their beautiful Christmas presents down before her.

Peter was delighted and, oh, the joy there was when he led his little sister home on Christmas day, and showed all the wonderful presents to his mother and father!

The Christmas Monks always kept Peter in their employ —in fact he is there to this day. And his parents, and his little sister who was entirely cured of her lameness, have never wanted for anything.

The First Christmas Tree in New England

From "The First Christmas Tree in New England," by Sarah J. Pritchard. Published in *St. Nicholas,* December 1887.   10 minutes

It was a November afternoon in 1635 and Mrs. Olcott was spinning flax in the cheerful kitchen of a small house near Plymouth Rock in Massachusetts. Her husband, Captain Olcott, had sailed from Boston three years before and neither he nor his ship had been heard from since, so had been given up for lost. But Mrs. Olcott kept up a brave heart and cheerful face for the sake of her children, Robert, Rupert, Lucy, and poor crippled little Roger.

One night as she sat by Roger's bed to sing him to sleep, he said as he often had before, "Tell me more about England, Mother."

So she told him of Christmas and the way they used to keep it in England before she became a Puritan—of her father's house and the rejoicings at Christmas time, and last of all about the great evergreen bough that was lighted with tapers and hung with gifts for the children.

As the Christmas season drew near, in all that Puritan land there was not a Christmas tree, not even a Christmas gift. Mrs. Olcott could not withstand Roger's wish to see a Christmas bough, so she told the two boys, Robert and Rupert, and little Lucy, what she was going to do.

"Oh, mother!" exclaimed Robert, the eldest son. "They'll persecute you to death; they'll drive us into the wilderness; we shall lose our home and everything."

"Remember, boys, your mother has been into the wilderness once, and she isn't afraid of that. We shall have the Christmas bough! I am going up to Boston tomorrow if the day is fine, and I'll bring back some nice little trinkets for poor Roger. Maybe a ship has come in lately; one is expected."

In the morning Mrs. Olcott set forth for Boston. She had not been there since the day she went to see the ship sail with her husband on it—the ship that never had been heard from since. That was more than three years before and it was on the way home that Roger had been so badly hurt that his little life was spoiled.

Great was the astonishment in the village of Plymouth when it was learned that the Widow Olcott had gone to Boston without saying anything to the neighbors. Why had she gone? She had no relatives there. What was she going to buy? Mrs. Hawley, a neighbor, went down the hill that same day to inquire, as soon as Mrs. Olcott was back, but found out very little.

As soon as the neighbor had gone Mrs. Olcott called the boys and bade them go to the pine woods and get the finest, handsomest young hemlock that they could find. "Get one that is straight and tall and well branched, and put it where you can draw it into the woodshed after dark," said she.

The boys went to the forest on Pine Hill and there they picked out the finest young tree on all the hill, and said, "We will take this one." So with their hatchets they hewed it down, and brought it safely home that night after dark. And when Roger was quietly sleeping they dragged the tree into the kitchen. It was too tall so they had to cut off a foot or two at the base. They pulled the curtains over the windows and fastened blankets over them to be sure no one could see in, and double-barred the door so no one could come in. Then they propped up the tree so it stood tall and straight in the kitchen.

Very early the next morning, while the stars shone on the snow covered hills—the same stars that shone sixteen hundred years before on the hills when Christ was born in Bethlehem—the little Puritan mother in New England arose very softly. She went out and lit the kitchen fire anew from the ash-covered embers. She fastened upon the branches of the tree the gifts she had bought in Boston. Then she took as many as twenty pieces of candle and fixed them upon the branches. After that, she softly called Rupert, Robert and Lucy, and told them to get up and dress and come into the kitchen.

Hurrying back, she began to light the candles with a bit of burning stick. Just as the last one was set aflame, in trooped the three children. Before they had time to say a word, they were silenced by their mother's warning.

"I wish to fetch Roger in and wake him up before it," she said. "Keep still until I come back!"

The little lad, fast asleep, was lifted in a blanket and gently carried into the kitchen.

"See! Roger, my boy, see!" she said, arousing him. "It is Christmas morning now! In England they have only Christmas boughs, but here in New England we have a whole Christmas tree!"

"O Mother!" he cried. "O Lucy! Is it really, really true, and no dream at all? Yes, I see! I see! O Mother! it is *so* beautiful! Were all the trees on the hills lighted up that way when Christ was born? And, Mother," he added, clapping his little hands with joy at the thought, "the stars *did* sing when Christ was born! They must be glad, then, and keep Christmas, too, in Heaven. I *know* they must, and there will be good times there."

"Yes," said his mother, "there will be good times there."

"What is that noise, Mother?" cried Roger.

What was it they heard? The little Olcott house had never before seemed to tremble so. There was tapping at the window; there was knocking at the door, and it was as yet scarcely break of day. There was a voice also shouting to someone.

"Shall I put out the candles, Mother?" whispered Robert.

"What will they do to us for having the tree?" asked Rupert.

Pale and white, Mrs. Olcott stood ready to meet her fate, until above the knocking she heard a voice calling, "Rachel! Rachel! Rachel!"

"Unbar the door!" she cried. "It's your father calling!"

The door was unbarred and in walked Captain Olcott amid shouting and laughter. He was followed ere long by every man and woman in Plymouth who had heard the good news of the arrival in Boston of the long-lost ship and Captain Olcott with it.

For a while nothing was thought of but the welcoming of the captain. But when the first excitement was over, they noticed the tall hemlock standing in the kitchen with all its candles ablaze, its gifts still hanging on it.

"What's this? What is it? What *does* this mean?" was asked again and again.

"It's welcome home to father!" said Lucy, her only thought to protect her mother.

"No, child, *no*!" sternly spoke Mrs. Olcott. "Tell the truth."

"It's—a—Christmas tree," faltered poor Lucy.

One after another, Pilgrims and Puritans, they all drew near and gazed and gazed. Their faces slowly softened into smiles as little Roger's piping voice rang out:

"She made it for me, mother did. But you may have it now, and all the pretty things that are on it, too, because you've brought my father back again."

Neither Pilgrim nor Puritan frowned at the gift. One man, the sternest, broke off a little twig and said, "I'll take it for the sake of the good old times at home."

Then every one wanted to take a bit for the same reason, until the young pine was bereft of half its branches. But still it stood, like a hero at his post, candles burning and gifts hanging, until all their guests had departed. The Olcotts were so grateful for the greatest gift—their father's safe return, that no gift was taken from the tree, until they had been told every bit of the story of his long, long voyage in a storm-beaten and disabled ship, which he, at last, had been able to guide safely into port. This was the ship that Mrs. Olcott had hoped would arrive in time for her Christmas tree.

The Left-Handed Christmas

From "The Left-Handed Christmas," by Toni Hult.
Published in *Adventure Trails for Boys and Girls,* December 1945. Reproduced by permission.   14 minutes

Six-year-old Sally climbed upon her father's lap so that she would be sure to hear the weather report. The Nelson family, clustered around the radio, waited almost impatiently for the Christmas carols to sign off.

"Here it comes now!" the children announced.

"Christmas day, continued low temperatures but clear with strong fresh winds," said the sure-sounding voice.

"Thank goodness!" Mrs. Nelson eased her plump weight into a nearby rocker.

The family looked at her in amazement. Father Nelson demanded, "Whatever for?"

Mother Nelson heaved a sigh of relief. "Santa Claus would've caught us left handed, for sure, if we'd been snowbound in this ranch house on Christmas day."

"Why? Is Santa Claus left handed?" Sally demanded.

Mother explained carefully. "You see, Sally, a storm has been heading this way the last twelve hours. Now it's going to by-pass this ranch, and we'll get to Grandpa's house tomorrow for Christmas all right."

"You mean there was a chance," Marge (who was fifteen) stopped putting her hair up on curlers, "of our missing out on Christmas at Grandpa's?"

"Why, all our presents are at Gramp's!" Jean and Joan, the twins, sputtered. It would be awful, they stormed, if they missed not only the gifts but all the cousins, uncles, and aunts—forty in all—as well as the turkey.

"But why does Santa Claus have to go and catch us left handed?" Sally persisted.

"He doesn't." Mother put Sally on her lap. "Caught left handed means not ready—well—to cook a Christmas dinner. You see when the aunts and cousins divided up the menu, we were supposed to bring home-baked bread, cream, butter, and eggs for the whole crowd, because we are the only ones who live on a ranch."

"I see," said Sally. "Then if we get to Grandpa's Santa Claus won't find us left handed."

"That's it." Mother laughingly brushed Sally off her lap and reached for the alarm clock. She set it for five o'clock. She would need every bit of that time to bake bread for forty people.

The four girls trooped up to bed, sure they would not sleep a wink. They took one last peep at the new Christmas dresses they'd be wearing tomorrow. "Ruffles, low necks, and short sleeves. Umm! You can wear things like that in Grandpa's steam-heated house," said Marge happily.

Early next morning Mrs. Nelson sat up with a start, although the alarm hadn't gone off yet. The window was closed, yet the shades were banging. She got out of bed and peeked out of the window. A twelve-inch ridge of dusty snow had drifted on the ledge. She couldn't see any of the telegraph poles along the railroad track. A storm was really raging.

Left handed, indeed! The weatherman, for once, was wrong. She dressed quickly and hurried down to the kitchen. Opening the storm door she looked out. The sky was like an angry giant spitting snow bullets, and his breath, vicious and gray-white, puffed furiously at haystacks, swirling the tops in all directions.

She pushed the door shut and stared at the great crocks of sponge she'd set the night before. Should she throw it out? She couldn't abide waste. Yet if she baked bread for forty people and there were only six to eat it, that, too, would be a waste.

The door opened and down trailed four sleepy girls.

"Merry Christmas!" Mrs. Nelson tried to sound cheerful.

They nodded, and mumbling a Merry Christmas, they dragged their feet to the window. They scratched a peekhole in the furry layer of frost so that they could see out.

Mr. Nelson came in, his head muffled in a huge woolen scarf. "Temperature's still falling," he announced. "Two below when I went out, and now it's down to six." The girls all but glared at him.

"Aw, cheer up," he coaxed. "The sun may come out yet."

Mrs. Nelson, hoping for the best, soon had all the work tables in the pantry and kitchen filled with puffing loaves of whole wheat and white bread. With experienced hands she now deftly shaped cinnamon rolls, butter twists and tea rolls.

When the wind suddenly swept down and shook the chimney like a big bad wolf, Sally wept. "Oh, why did Santa Claus have to catch us left handed?"

Her daddy tried to comfort her. "Tell you what," he said, "if Train No. 42 can make it, why, I believe our car can." He went to the phone to call the station master, but the line was dead.

The girls ran to the north window and began scratching at the frost again to watch for the eight-thirty train.

Nine o'clock. Ten o'clock. Eleven o'clock, no train.

At a quarter after, Marge gave a shout. She saw the cloud of smoke first. It poured heavily from the smokestack and then curled back into a big plume nearly concealing the three cars.

Mrs. Nelson was worried. "Dad, do you think we should try it? That bridge down in the cut! There have been so many accidents there."

"We'll take shovels along, and we'll stop at Prince Albert's and ask him to stand by."

"But . . ."

41

"Anyway," he explained, "not a lot of snow has fallen. It's just that the wind has piled it up in great drifts."

"Well that's just it . . ." She shook her head. Those drifts—you know how treacherous they are. The car might pass right over them and then again it might break through."

"Yes, I know," he said seriously. "But the wind has swept the highway practically clear except for the cuts, and when we get to them I'll get out and shovel."

Mrs. Nelson shook her head again, and walked to the north window. It was considerably lighter now. Sure enough the prairie was practically clean. "Well," she agreed, "maybe after all . . ." She was scraping a little more frost from the window. "Oh, look Dad!" she cried, pointing to the east where the railroad curved sharply.

Of all the miserable luck! No. 42 was stuck in a snowdrift.

If No. 42 couldn't make it, neither could their car.

It was up to Mrs. Nelson to figure out a Christmas dinner. In the cellar she studied the jars of processed beef, the sugar cured ham, and the steamed puddings she'd cooked up to last them the winter. In spite of being caught left handed she managed a fine Christmas dinner, yet no one had any appetite for it.

The afternoon lagged drearily. They tried guessing games, but today there was no fun in it.

Popping corn was much better. When the dishpan was heaping full, all of a sudden the sun peeped sheepishly from under the western edge of the gray sky blanket.

"You ought to be ashamed of yourself," Sally yelled to the sun. The girls laughed for the first time, and then the sun really came out and sent the clouds scuttling off in all directions.

At the same time from the east came Prince Albert on a fat white horse with a crazy quilt for a saddle. He wasn't really a prince, just Mr. Kummering, a plump Dutch bachelor who lived on the adjoining ranch. Sally called him that because of the round label, with "Prince Albert" printed on it, that dangled from his tobacco pouch.

Mr. Nelson opened the kitchen door. "Hey, Neighbor, take your mare into the barn and come on in."

"Been trying to phone you all afternoon," Prince Albert said, stamping his feet as Dad helped brush off the snow with the kitchen broom.

"I know," Mr. Nelson nodded. "Wires are down."

"Yah, I seen 'em. Between our places. Station agent sent me over."

"Station agent! Whatever for?"

"No. 42's stuck down at the curve."

Well, for goodness sakes! They looked at Prince Albert in amazement. Of all the ridiculous things for him to ride over just to tell them that. As if they didn't know. He cleared his throat. "Lot of people on that train. Maybe seventy-five or eighty. Haven't had any food all day."

Mr. and Mrs. Nelson looked at each other with conscience stricken eyes. Here they'd been so busy with their own gloom they hadn't given a thought to anyone else.

Mrs. Nelson leaped to her feet. "We must get 'em something hot right away. But what?"

"Potatoes," Prince Albert suggested.

Jean and Joan ran for the big pan. "We'll bake em," they decided. "Then we won't have to peel 'em." They lifted the trap door in the floor and disappeared down the stairs.

"Better bring up the Sand Hill potatoes," Mother called. "They bake in about thirty minutes."

"What'll we do for dishes?" Marge asked. "We don't have that many."

"In the milk house!" Sally shouted. They laughed. Sure enough. While the kitchen over at the church was being repainted, the community dishes had been stored in Nelson's milk house.

43

"Dishes will be my job." Dad reached for his leather jacket.

"I'll hook the team to the wagon," offered Prince Albert. "You want the big grays?"

"Sure. But no hurry—warm yourself first. The food isn't ready yet. Then be sure to throw a lot of hay into the wagon box and get the auto robes out of the car."

Mrs. Nelson climbed up on the kitchen stool and brought down the huge canning kettle. "I'll fix the meat. Six people to the quart. Six into eighty is about thirteen." She called to the twins. "Bring up six half-gallons and one quart of the processed beef. We'll heat it up in the jars and it'll stay hot that way."

"The Lord was with me when I baked all that bread!" Mother exclaimed, dropping the jars of meat into the boiling water.

Jean and Joan rolled eighty-five huge potatoes into the big oven of the kitchen range and got out dill pickles and beets.

The door opened and Father came in with another armful of fire wood. "Dishes are all packed and in the wagon. Ummm," he sniffed. "Smells good. I could eat again!"

"Me, too." Prince Albert turned red like the beet pickles for being so bold.

"Got an idea," Dad remarked. "We'll have a picnic on the train on Christmas day."

"But, Mother," Marge cried, "there's no dessert!"

"Oh, yes, there is." Dad decided definitely. "Plum pudding!" So Marge hurriedly made a hot fruit juice sauce to pour over it.

"At last everything's about ready." Mother fanned herself with the corner of her starched apron.

Soon they were all tucked in the wagon and the horses, glad to get out, raced across the prairie, somehow dodging snowdrifts until they reached the railroad curve. Prince Albert bounced alongside on his white mare.

44

"Oh, perhaps they'll give us a train ride," Sally suggested.

"Of all the crazy ideas." The twins giggled.

When the wagon came alongside the snorting locomotive, the horses reared up on their hind legs. The engine frightened Sally, too.

"Oh, dear," she said, "if they do offer us a ride, we won't have to take it, will we, Daddy?"

"Don't worry, Baby!" He seesawed the lines until the horses were again in hand. "They aren't likely to, stuck in that drift!"

The passengers watched them, glad for any diversion. When they saw food they laughed and cried, then everyone pitched in to help.

"Picnic nothing!" exclaimed the conductor, his plate filled with hot food. "This is a Christmas feast. The most appreciated one I've ever had."

"You've certainly earned it," said one man. "You've done a good job keeping us from getting too discouraged. Where do you get your good humor?"

Sally liked the jolly conductor and moved over close to him. He rescued her plum pudding, ready to drip over the edge of her plate and seemed to understand a little girl.

"And does your Mrs. Conductor have to eat all by herself?" Sally asked.

Everyone laughed, except the conductor. "No," he said, "you see she has the little ones to keep her company."

Sally's face lit up. "Oh, are there little conductors, too?" Everyone laughed harder than ever. Sally looked at them. No, they didn't seem to be laughing at her. It must be they were laughing because everyone was happy. Then she laughed, too.

Suddenly the conductor stopped eating. "Look!" He pointed to the east where a column of smoke was approaching.

45

The snowplow! At last! Soon the track would be cleared and No. 42 would be on its way.

"Back the train up an eighth of a mile or more," he ordered the engineer. "The snowplow will have to make a run for it if it's going to make any headway at all through that drift."

"Goody," Sally shouted as the train moved. "We're going to have a train ride after all."

"She would get her way!" the twins giggled.

Then everybody began cheering and yelling.

The train stopped, and the men helped pack the boxes of dishes in the hay of the wagon box.

"Well, Sally," the conductor asked, "who would you like to have carry you to the wagon?"

She looked at all the smiling men. "You," she said, without hesitation.

"You're elected!" The men grinned.

The passengers and crew waved good-by and the wagon bumped over the prairie, with Prince Albert trotting ahead this time so he'd be ready to open the ranch gate for them.

"What a perfectly wonderful Christmas!" Jean exclaimed.

"One we'll never forget!" Joan added.

"About the only important thing we lost out on was the Christmas caroling," Margie sighed.

"Let's sing 'em now," suggested the twins. "You take the high part and we'll harmonize."

"It came upon the midnight clear . . ." they began softly.

Sally knew the tune but not all the words, yet she sang loudest of all. She was sleepy now, and snuggled closer to her mother. "It was fun, wasn't it," she murmured, "to have a left-handed Christmas?"

Where the Christmas Tree Grew

From the story by Mary E. Wilkins Freeman.
Published in *St. Nicholas*, January 1888.   12 minutes

It was afternoon recess at No. 4 District School, in Warner. There was a heavy snowstorm, so several children were in the warm schoolroom. There were five or six little girls and one boy. The girls, with the exception of Jenny Brown, were trim and sweet in their winter dresses and neat school aprons. The one boy lounged against the blackboard, his dark face all aglow as he talked.

"Yes, it does—*honest!*" said he.

The other girls nudged one another softly; but Jenny Brown stood with her innocent, solemn eyes fixed upon Earl Munroe's face, drinking in every word.

"You ask anybody who knows," continued Earl. "Ask Judge Barker, ask—the minister—."

"Oh!" cried the other little girls, but the boy shook his head impatiently at them.

"Why, look here, it's nothing more than *reasonable* that Christmas trees grow wild with the presents all on 'em! What sense would there be in 'em if they didn't, I'd like to know? They grow in different places, of course; but these around here grow mostly on the mountain over there. They come up every spring, and they all blossom out about Christmas time, and folks go hunting them to give to the children. Father and Ben are over on the mountain today—"

"Oh, oh!" cried the little girls.

Jenny Brown had a little, round, simple face. Her thin brown hair was combed back and braided tightly in one tiny braid tied with a bit of shoestring. Her dress was of a faded green color; it was scalloped and bound around the

47

bottom, and had some green ribbon bows down the front, evidently handed down from some grown-up.

Jenny Brown was eight, and small for her age—a strange, gentle, ignorant little girl, never doubting the truth of what she was told, so she believed every word of the mischievous boy's tale.

This was her first term at school, and she had never before seen much of other children. She had lived her eight years all alone at home with her mother, and had never been told about Christmas. Her mother had other things to think about. She worked hard, doing washing and cleaning. Sometimes the Browns had almost enough to eat, at other times they half starved. It was half-starving time just then. Jenny had not had enough to eat that day. There was a pinched look on the little face upturned toward Earl Munroe's. Jenny had always regarded him with awe and admiration.

Earl Munroe was quite the king of this little district school. He was the son of the wealthiest man in town. Earl himself realized his importance and had at times the loftiness of a young prince in his manner. The boy was really pleasant and generous hearted, but enjoyed being lordly once in a while, that was all.

Soon the bell rang, and they all filed to their seats and lessons were begun. After school was over, Earl stood in the door when Jenny passed by.

"Say, Jenny," he called, "when are you going over the mountain to find a Christmas tree? You'd better go pretty soon, or they'll be gone."

"That's so!" chimed in one of the girls. "You'd better go right off, Jenny."

Jenny passed along, her face shyly dimpling with her little innocent smile, and said nothing. She had quite a long walk to her home. As she waded along, she could see the mountain always before her. This road led straight to it, then turned and wound around its base. It had stopped snowing and the sun was setting clear. Jenny kept her eyes fixed on the mountain.

There was no school the next day, for it was the day before Christmas. It was pleasant and not very cold. The little village stores were crowded. Sleds trailing Christmas greens went flying; people were hastening with parcels under their arms, their hands full. Jenny Brown was out too. She was climbing Franklin Mountain, peering through those white fairy columns and arches for—a Christmas tree.

That night, the mountain had turned rosy, and faded, and the stars were coming out, when a frantic woman, panting, crying out in her distress, went running up the road to the Munroe's. Then she burst into the house and threw open the dining room door, crying out in gasps:

"Hev you seen her? My Jenny's lost! She's lost! Oh, Oh, Oh! They said they saw her comin' up this way, this mornin'. *Hev* you seen her? *Hev* you?"

Earl and his father and mother were having tea in the handsome oak-paneled dining room. Earl sat as if frozen. Mrs. Brown had been at work all day; when she returned, Jenny was gone. Someone had seen her going up the road to the Munroes' that morning about ten o'clock. That was her only clew.

Earl saw his mother draw the poor woman into the room and try to comfort her; he heard his father order the horses to be harnessed immediately. When Mr. Munroe opened the door, Earl, with his coat and cap on, was at his heels.

"Why, you can't go, Earl!" said his father, when he saw him. "Go back at once."

Earl was white and trembling. He half sobbed. "Oh, Father, I must go! I—*I believe I know where she is!*"

Then his father faced sharply around, and Earl told his ridiculous, childish, and cruel little story. "I—didn't dream —she'd really be—such a little—goose as to—go," he choked out, "but she must have. I know she believed every word I told her."

Jenny's mother screamed, "Oh, if she's lost on the mountain, they'll never find her! They never will!"

Earl gave a despairing glance at her, and bolted upstairs to his own room, and lying face downward on his bed, cried as if his heart would break. Presently, he crawled downstairs and into the parlor. The Christmas tree stood in the bay window. It was quite small that year, only for the family, but it was well laden. After tea, the presents were to have been distributed. There were some for the father and mother, and some for the servants, but the bulk of them were for Earl.

By and by, his mother, who had heard him come downstairs, peeped into the room, and saw him busily taking his presents from the tree. Her heart sank with sad displeasure and amazement. She would not have believed that her boy could be so utterly selfish as to think of Christmas presents *then*. But she said nothing.

Morning came at last, and Mr. Munroe with it. No success so far. He drank some coffee and was off again. That was quite early. An hour or two later, the breakfast bell rang. Earl did not respond to it, so his mother went to the foot of the stairs and called him. When Earl did not answer, she went upstairs, and found that he was not in his room. Then she looked in the parlor, and stood staring in bewilderment. Earl was not there, but neither was the Christmas tree nor his presents—they had vanished bodily!

Just at that moment Earl Munroe was hurrying down the road, dragging his big sled, on which were loaded his Christmas presents and the Christmas tree. On every one of those neat parcels, above his own name, was written in his big, crooked, childish hand, "Jenny Brown, from—" Earl Munroe had not saved one Christmas present for himself.

Pulling the sled along, his cheeks brilliant, his eyes glowing, he met Maud Barker. She was Judge Barker's daughter, and the girl who had joined him in advising Jenny to hunt on the mountain for the Christmas tree. Maud carried a new beaver muff, but in one hand only. The other dangled mittenless at her side; it was pink with cold, but on its third finger sparkled a new gold ring with a blue stone in it.

"Oh, Earl!" she called out, "Have they found Jenny Brown? I was going up to your house to—Why, Earl Munroe, what have you got there?"

"I'm carrying my Christmas presents and the tree up to Jenny's—so she'll find 'em when she comes back," said the boy, flushing red. There was a little defiant choke in his voice.

"Why, what for?"

"I rather think they belong to her, more'n they do to me, after what's happened."

"Does your mother know?"

"No, she wouldn't care. She'd think I was only doing what I ought."

Earl was passing on when a thought struck him.

"Say, Maud," he cried eagerly, "Haven't you something you can put in? Girls' things might please her better, you know. Some of mine are—rather queer, I'm afraid. There's a lot of candy and oranges and figs and books; there's one by Jules Verne I guess she'll like; but there's a great big jack-knife, and—a brown velvet bicycle suit."

"Why, Earl Munroe! What could she do with a bicycle suit?"

"I thought, maybe, she could rip the seams an' sew 'em some way, or something. Don't you s'pose she could?" Earl asked anxiously.

"I don't know; her mother could tell," said Maud.

"Well, I'll hang it on, anyhow. Maud, haven't you anything to give her?"

"I don't know." Earl eyed her sharply.

"Isn't that muff new," he asked. "And that ring?"

Maud nodded. "She'd be delighted with 'em. Oh, Maud, put 'em in!"

Maud looked at him. Her pretty mouth quivered a little, her blue eyes filled with tears.

"I don't believe my mother would let me," she faltered. "Come with me, and I'll ask her."

"All right," said Earl, with a tug at his sled rope.

He waited with his load in front of Maud's house until she came forth radiant, lugging a big basket. She had her last winter's red cashmere dress, a hood, some mittens, cake and biscuit and nice slices of cold meat.

"Mother said these would be much more suitable for her," said Maud.

Over across the street another girl stood at the gate, waiting for news.

"Have they found her?" she cried. "Where are you going with all those things?"

Somehow, Earl's generous, romantic impulse spread like an epidemic. This little girl soon came flying out with her contribution; then there were more—quite a little procession finally filed down the road to Jenny Brown's house.

The idea never entered their heads that little, innocent, trustful Jenny might never come home to see the Christmas tree which they set up in her poor home.

It was no surprise whatever when they saw, about noon, Mr. Munroe's sleigh, with Jenny and her mother and Mrs. Munroe, drive up to the door.

Afterward, they heard how a woodcutter had found Jenny crying, over on the east side of the mountain, at sunset, and had taken her home with him. He lived five miles from the village, and was an old man, not able to walk so far that night to tell them of her safety. His wife had been very good to the child. Next forenoon, some of the searchers had met the old man plodding along the mountain road with the news.

52

When Jenny reached home the children shouted to her to come in quick! They pulled her into the room where they had been at work. Then the child stood with her hands clasped, staring at the Christmas tree. All too far away had she been searching for it. The Christmas tree grew not on the wild mountainside, in the lonely woods, but at home, close to warm, loving hearts; and that was where she found it.

Easter

The Baker's Top-Hat Bunny

From the story by Robert L. Grimes. Published in *Jack and Jill*, April 1942. Reproduced by permission.

10 minutes

"Next Sunday is Easter," said Mr. Oofendorf to his wife. "We'll have a busy week in our cake and candy shop."

"Make lots of nice things for Easter," ordered his wife. "We must earn much money."

Mr. Oofendorf was short and fat and very kind. "Money isn't everything," he said to himself, as he began to get ready for Easter.

For several days, the baker worked hard in his shop. He made hot cross buns and cake lambs and pies and butter cookies in the bakery. In the candy shop he made chocolate bunnies and hens and chicks, and a whole bushel basketful of candy Easter eggs.

All of these things he put into just one of his store windows. The other window he left empty.

"But this is wrong!" cried his wife. "How can we make money with one window bare?"

"I'm working on something special for the other window," said the baker, smiling.

"What?"

"My idea of Easter."

"Silly man! Everybody knows what Easter is for. For selling hams and fresh eggs and bakery goods. For making money."

"No, that isn't what Easter stands for," murmured Mr. Oofendorf. But he was afraid to say it out loud.

On the evening of Good Friday, the one shop window was still bare. But early Saturday morning, Mr. Oofendorf might have been seen scurrying about. He trotted back and forth from kitchen to window. Finally he was through. He called to his wife, "Come and see. This is my idea of Easter."

His wife looked. There in the shop window was a big nest of paper grass. And on the nest there was a huge chocolate Easter egg, with the top broken out. Standing in the egg was a rabbit, made of cake and covered with white coconut fur. His eyes were licorice drops. One of them was partly closed, as if he were winking. And cocked between his ears, the bunny wore a black top hat. In his paws he held a basket, full of candy vegetables and fruits— candy carrots, candy corn, candy radishes, and cherries, peaches and plums.

The baker's wife looked at the window a long time. "Well!" she said. "So *that's* your idea of Easter. A top-hatted rabbit! How much can we get for it?"

The baker hesitated, then he said, "I thought maybe two dollars—"

"What!" cried the wife. "Two dollars? Why, you've put more than two dollars' worth of good cake and candy in that window, besides your hours and hours of work. Two dollars, indeed! You'd better ask ten dollars!"

"Yes, my dear," said Mr. Oofendorf meekly. He wrote "$10.00" on a price tag and placed it on the bunny's hat.

"And sell it to the very first customer you can," continued his wife.

But Mr. Oofendorf wasn't so anxious to sell the bunny. He wanted people to see it in his window and to understand how he felt about Easter.

He went inside his shop and waited for customers. Ah, here came a man. His arms were full of bundles. "I want a box of candy for my children," said the man crossly.

58

"That's all Easter ever amounts to at our house. Candy, candy, candy . . . ."

Mr. Oofendorf wrapped a box of candy and gave it to the customer. The man paid for the candy and went out, not even glancing at the Top-Hat Bunny.

The baker shook his head and said to himself, "My wife thinks Easter is for making money. And that man's children think Easter is for getting lots of candy."

Just then the baker's wife came in from the kitchen. "Any customers yet for that winking rabbit?"

"No, my dear. But there will be. In the big crowds on the street this afternoon, someone will understand the bunny and will want to buy him."

But that afternoon the sun went under a cloud, the wind blew, and it began to rain. People hurried along, hats pulled down, umbrellas held low. They had no time to look at top-hatted rabbits.

All afternoon it rained. Once a woman came in and asked for a chocolate cake. She was one of Mr. Oofendorf's old customers, and he knew her quite well. After her cake was wrapped, the baker said, "Would you care to buy the Top-Hat Bunny?"

The lady sniffed. "If I had ten dollars, I'd buy myself a new hat and gloves."

"But the hat and gloves you're wearing look very nice," said Mr. Oofendorf.

The lady sniffed again. "They're all right to wear on a Saturday shopping trip," she said, "but tomorrow is Easter, and if I had a new hat I could go walking to show off my grand clothes."

Mr. Oofendorf said nothing. But when the lady had gone out, he murmured to himself, "Easter isn't for making money, and it isn't for getting candy. And it isn't for showing off."

Mrs. Oofendorf came in just then, and scolded again about the rabbit.

"But it shows what Easter stands for," said the baker.

"That's what you keep saying," said his wife. "But what *does* it stand for?"

Mr. Oofendorf looked thoughtful. "I'm not sure that I know," he said. "But you wait. Some customer will understand the Top-Hat Bunny."

"Understand it!" said his wife. "We will be better off if someone buys it."

Mr. Oofendorf looked sad as his wife returned to the back part of the shop.

The next customer who came into the bakery was a tired messenger boy. He was delivering flowers for a greenhouse. As he entered the shop the messenger put down two big flower pots, tall white lilies wrapped in fancy paper. Beside the two plants, the boy put down a long box that must have been filled with cut flowers.

The messenger boy bought two cupcakes, and ate them right in the shop. "This gives me a chance to rest," he said, "and am I tired! And I still have to go to the other end of town." He nodded toward the flowers he had put down. "All those for one house," he said.

When the messenger boy had gone out, Mr. Oofendorf shook his head. "Easter isn't for getting loads of flowers, either," he said to himself.

Outside the shop, it was still raining. As the baker watched, a thin-faced boy came up to the window with a girl just a little smaller than himself. His sister, probably. They looked in at the Top-Hat Bunny and talked about it.

Mr. Oofendorf thought of getting a hot cross bun for each of the children, but just then they went away from the window. "Well, anyway, they seemed to like the Top-Hat Bunny," decided the baker.

It was almost evening, now. Customers came and went, but no one bought the Top-Hat Bunny. Then, just as Mr. Oofendorf was about to close his shop, the children who had liked the Top-Hat Bunny came by again. This time they were with a young woman. She looked tired, and her coat was shabby. The boy and girl brought the woman over to the shop window. The three of them looked at the Top-Hat Bunny, and then they all smiled. Mr. Oofendorf decided that the young woman must be the children's mother. "Probably she has been working all day and the children went to meet her," thought the baker.

Now the woman opened her purse and gave the boy a coin. Then the shop door opened and the two children came in. "Mother gave us a dime for Easter eggs," said the boy. "She says we can pick them out while she goes to the grocery."

Mr. Oofendorf began filling a sack with candy eggs. "I saw you looking at the Top-Hat Bunny," he said to the children. "Do you like him?"

"He's wonderful!" cried the boy. "You know, I've made up a story about that bunny. The broken chocolate egg stands for winter, which is over. The top hat and the bunny's wink mean you should always dress as nice as you can, and be jolly. The vegetables mean that spring will soon be here, and there'll be lots of nice things for us in the garden. It's Easter—and spring!"

"Bless me!" cried the baker. "Just my idea about Easter too! You ought to buy the Top-Hat Bunny!"

"Oh, I couldn't," said the boy. "The tag says ten dollars."

"Dear me, does it say that?" cried Mr. Oofendorf. "What a mistake! I wrote a *dollar* sign and it should be *cents*." He took a pencil and changed the tag.

The children jumped about in excitement. "Ten cents for the Top-Hat Bunny! We'll take him instead of the candy eggs!"

A little later Mrs. Oofendorf stepped in. She looked at the bare window. "So you sold the rabbit. Who bought it?"

61

"A young gentleman and his sister," answered the baker. "And they knew what the Top-Hat Bunny stood for!"

"Did you get ten dollars for him?"

Mr. Oofendorf was so happy that he was no longer afraid of his wife. "I sold the bunny for ten cents," he said. "Money isn't everything! And candy and new clothes and flowers aren't everything, either. But spring is here; new life is coming to the world. And *that's* practically everything, at Easter time!"

The Loveliest Rose in the World

From *Stories and Tales,* by Hans Christian Andersen.   5 minutes

Once there reigned a queen, in whose garden were
found the most glorious flowers at all seasons and from
all the lands of the world. But more than all others she
loved the roses, and she had many kinds, from the wild
dog rose with its apple-scented green leaves to the most
splendid, large, crimson roses. They grew against the
garden walls, wound themselves around the pillars and
window frames, and crept through the windows into the
rooms, and all along the ceilings in the halls. And the
roses were of many colors, and of every fragrance and
form.

But care and sorrow dwelt in those halls. The queen
lay upon a sick bed, and the doctors said she must die.

"There is still one thing that can save her," said the
wisest of them. "Bring her the loveliest rose in the world,
the rose that is the symbol of the purest, the brightest
love. If that is held before her eyes ere they close, she
will not die."

Then old and young came from every side with roses,
the loveliest that bloomed in each garden, but they were not
of the right sort. The flower was to be plucked from
the Garden of Love. But what rose in all that garden
expressed the highest and purest love?

The poets sang of the loveliest rose in the world—of
the love of maid and youth, and of the love of dying heroes.

"But they have not named the right flower," said the
wise man. "They have not pointed out the place where

it blooms in its splendor. It is not the rose that springs from the hearts of youthful lovers, though this rose will ever be fragrant in song. It is not the bloom that sprouts from the blood flowing from the breast of the hero who dies for his country, though few deaths are sweeter than his, and no rose is redder than the blood that flows then. Nor is it the wondrous flower to which man devotes many a sleepless night and much of his fresh life—the magic flower of silence."

"But I know where it blooms," said a happy mother, who came with her pretty child to the bedside of the dying queen. "I know where the loveliest rose of love may be found. It springs in the blooming cheeks of my sweet child, when, waking from sleep, he opens his eyes and smiles tenderly at me."

"Lovely is this rose, but there is one that is lovelier still," said the wise man.

"I have seen the loveliest, purest rose that blooms," said a woman. "I saw it on the cheeks of the queen. She had taken off her golden crown. And in the long, dreary night she carried her sick child in her arms. She wept, kissed it, and prayed for her child."

"Holy and wonderful is the white rose of a mother's grief," answered the wise man, "but it is not the one we seek."

"The loveliest rose in the world I saw at the altar of the Lord," said the good Bishop, "the young maidens went to the Lord's table. Roses were blushing and pale roses shining on their fresh cheeks. A young girl stood there. She looked with all the love and purity of her spirit up to heaven. That was the expression of the highest and purest love."

"May she be blessed," said the wise man, "but not one of you has yet named the loveliest rose in the world."

Then there came into the room a child, the queen's little son.

"Mother," cried the boy, "only hear what I have read."

And the child sat by her bedside and read from the Book of Him who suffered death upon the cross to save men, and even those who were not yet born. "Greater love there is not."

And a rosy glow spread over the cheeks of the queen, and her eyes gleamed, for she saw that from the leaves of the Book there bloomed the loveliest rose, that sprang from the blood of Christ shed on the cross.

"I see it!" she said. "He who beholds this, the loveliest rose on earth, shall never die."

Pink Petunia

From the story by Seth Harmon. Published in
Children's Activities Magazine, April 1938. Reproduced
by permission.   13 minutes

All the shop windows in Upingham were decked out
for Easter. They were gay with fancy baskets, yellow
cotton chicks, and plaster rabbits. But one window was
most wonderful of all. For in it sat a beautiful live
bunny, nibbling a lettuce leaf and looking calmly out
through the glass.

An excited group of children had already gathered
before this window when Albert and Betty ran up.

"Just think! Tomorrow evening that rabbit will belong
to one of us!" cried one of the boys.

"It's no ordinary rabbit," another boy pointed out. "See
how long and soft its fur is!"

"Oh, I do hope our basket of Easter eggs wins in the
contest," Betty whispered to her brother. "Wouldn't you
just love to have that dear little rabbit?"

"I'm almost sure we will win it," replied Albert. "We'll
take ever so much pains to make our basket look nice."

The two children stood for a few moments watching
the fascinating little rabbit twitch its pink nose, and then
they hurried into the store around the corner.

Mr. Hicks, the proprietor, smiled at them and pointed
to a counter at one side.

"You don't even have to tell me what you youngsters
are after," he chuckled. "Easter egg dyes, of course, like
all the rest! Take your choice yonder. I have dyes of
all sorts."

The two children caught their breath with excitement at the beautiful array of colored envelopes that lay on the counter. Albert jingled the pennies in his pocket just to make sure he had taken them out of the little china bowl where he and his sister had been keeping them.

"This looks like an extra-fancy package," he told Betty as he eyed the gaudy illustration on one of the envelopes very critically.

He was thinking of all the baskets of colored eggs, besides theirs, that would be entered in the contest. Would this set of dyes, he wondered, make such a pretty basket that it would win the rabbit which the businessmen of the town were offering as a prize?

"I think this one is pretty, too," Betty said, pointing to another packet.

"Take all the time you want," Mr. Hicks said good naturedly as he turned to wait on two other children who had just entered the store.

Betty looked around. "It's Teddy and Jean Kramer," she said to Albert. "Jean's picking out flower seeds."

The Kramer children lived in a shabby house on a back street not far from Albert and Betty. Their father had been out of work for some time, and things hadn't been going very well with the family.

When Betty looked around again, her eyes met Jean's.

"Going to have some pretty flowers again this year?" Betty asked. "You had such wonderful morning-glories last year."

"The school gave us the seeds," Teddy said. "We're— we're not going to have flowers this year."

"I want these pretty flowers, Teddy," little Jean said, holding up a packet of pink petunias for her brother to look at.

"They are a specially fine variety," said Mr. Hicks. "They will grow anywhere. They have blossoms as big as roses."

Teddy counted out his pennies from a faded purse and handed them to Mr. Hicks and picked up his package of oatmeal. Then he turned toward the door.

"Come on, Jean," he said.

The little girl was still holding the package of choice petunia seeds in her hand as if she couldn't give up the pretty things. Her lips quivered, and tears sprang to her blue eyes as Teddy firmly took the package from her hand and laid it back on the counter.

"There's no use in crying for what we can't have, Sister," Teddy said not unkindly. And then, as he met the eyes of the two other children, he added proudly, "Anyway, it's much too early to plant petunias."

Betty and Albert watched the shabby little pair go out the door. Then they turned back to the pile of Easter egg dyes. But somehow they didn't look so interesting to Betty as they had looked before. She was thinking of the package of pink petunia seeds and of the tears in Jean's blue eyes.

"Well, have you children decided which package of colors will win the white rabbit?" Mr. Hicks said, smiling, as he went over to where the children were standing.

Betty pulled her brother's sleeve. "Let's go out and look at the bunny again before we decide," she whispered.

There was no one in front of the window where the rabbit was.

"Why did you want to come out here?" Albert asked wonderingly. "That won't help us to decide on the dyes."

"I—I don't think I care much if we don't have the bunny," Betty said, bravely blinking back a tear.

"Why, what do you mean?" asked Albert.

"I—I was just thinking that maybe we—we could get those petunia seeds for Jean and not bother about the dyes."

"Oh," said Albert.

"Don't you remember how everyone talked about Teddy's and Jean's morning-glories last year, and how much Jean loved them? It was the only pretty thing around there," Betty went on.

"We probably wouldn't win the contest anyway," said Albert, pretending not to care.

"And Jean would be so happy with the petunias," said Betty.

"It would be a lot of trouble to fix the eggs too," said Albert.

"Shall we get the seeds?" asked Betty.

"It's all right with me," agreed Albert, beginning to whistle.

In a minute the children were back in Mr. Hick's store.

"Well, have you decided?" he asked.

"We're not going to get any dyes," Albert said. "We've changed our minds."

Betty picked up the very packet of seeds that Teddy had taken from Jean a few moments before. Albert counted out his pennies and handed them to Mr. Hicks.

"We're going to get these seeds instead," he said.

"We'll put a card on it and say, 'From the Easter Bunny,'" said Betty as the children left the store, while Mr. Hicks stared after them.

"And we'll hang it on their door tonight so they'll get it in the morning," added Albert. Then they started for home. Albert had his hands in his pockets and was whistling loudly, while Betty was trying not to think how much she would like to snuggle a soft white bunny in her arms.

When they passed Grandma Kuller's cottage, the little old lady was out in her garden.

"Come in," she called out cheerily to her little friends. "I've just taken a pan of currant cookies out of the oven, and I want you to sample them for me!"

The children needed no second invitation. They had tasted Grandma Kuller's cookies before. So they followed

69

her into the house and were soon eating cookies and drinking milk in her tidy kitchen.

"I suppose every child in Upingham is dyeing Easter eggs today, getting ready for the contest," Grandma Kuller said.

Albert and Betty exchanged glances.

"My, my, how well I remember what Easter eggs meant to me in the old country!" Grandma Kuller went on. "On Easter Eve we youngsters all went to bed early, mind you, so that the big white Easter Hare could hide his colored eggs in our house. How we did scramble out of bed on Easter morning to get to our egg hunt!"

"What kind of dyes did you use?" Albert asked. He was still thinking about the gay packages on Mr. Hicks' counter.

"Indeed, we had no dyes such as you children have today," Grandma Kuller chuckled. "But I dare say no prettier or fancier eggs than ours were ever placed in an Easter nest. We used bits of bright figured calico to dye our eggs—like this apron or the curtains yonder."

"That must have been wonderful," said Betty.

"Is your basket ready for the contest?" Grandma Kuller asked after a moment.

The children's faces flushed.

"We're—we're not going to have any basket," Betty stammered.

"But I thought the other day you told me you were gathering sweet grass in the meadow to weave into a basket," Grandma Kuller persisted.

"We—we decided not to get any of Mr. Hicks' dyes," Albert said slowly.

There were a few moments of silence as Grandma Kuller's bright eyes looked first at one of the children and then the other.

Suddenly she jumped up from her chair. "Just wait a moment," she said briskly.

70

She pulled a little shawl over her head and was out of the door in a twinkling. In another minute, she was back with six white eggs in her apron.

"Fetch me that scrap bag from behind my sewing basket, Betty," she said, pointing to a bag of bright print.

The little girl hurried to obey. What in the world was Grandma Kuller going to do, she wondered.

"Now help me pick out the prettiest, brightest bits of calico we can find. And, Albert, you stir up the fire and get the kettle to boiling."

By this time Albert and Betty were bubbling with excitement. Whenever Grandma Kuller did anything, it was sure to be interesting.

"Thread a needle, Betty, and I'll show you how to sew a snug little calico coat around this egg," Grandma Kuller said.

Fingers flew at their tasks. In almost no time at all, six eggs were tightly sewed up inside their gayly colored wrappers, while smoke poured from the chimney as Albert stirred up the fire. Soon the kettle was singing a merry tune on the stove. Then the children very carefully dropped the eggs, one by one, into the bubbling water. Grandma Kuller took a sharp look at the clock on the mantel.

"We must time them just right," she said, "so that the design will come off clear and bright. My, my, this certainly makes me feel like a child again!"

At just the right moment, the six eggs were lifted out of the water and placed on the windowsill to cool. Their calico coats were faded and dull. For a moment the children looked worried. Where had all the pretty, bright colors gone?

Then Grandma Kuller clipped off the faded wrappers with her scissors—and there were the eggs—gay and colorful! The pretty designs from the calico were sharply printed on the eggs.

"Oh, how beautiful!" cried the children. "They're the very prettiest eggs we've ever seen!"

Grandma Kuller looked much pleased, "Take the eggs home with you," she said, "and make them look as pretty as possible in your basket of sweet grass. And who knows what will happen!"

The next day was Saturday. Betty and Albert arranged their basket carefully and entered it in the contest well before noon, the hour when the judges were to make their decision.

"Let's go over to Teddy's and Jean's and see if they found their package of seeds," suggested Betty.

When they reached the shabby little house, they found Teddy and Jean busily working in the back yard, getting ready to plant their petunias.

Little Jean looked up when she saw Betty. There were no tears in her blue eyes now. They were shining with happiness.

"See!" she cried. "See what the Easter Bunny brought to Brother and me!"

"It was an Easter Bunny, wasn't it?" said Betty, smiling.

"Shall I help you dig up that ground?" Albert asked Teddy.

Pretty soon the four children were so interested in getting the bed ready for the pink petunias that Albert and Betty forgot all about the contest.

Suddenly they saw a crowd of excited children running up the street toward them.

"Your basket won the contest! You got the white rabbit!" they kept shouting over and over again.

A few minutes later, Betty had the beautiful soft little white rabbit snuggled up close in her arms.

"Maybe that's the Easter Bunny that brought my pink petunias," cried little Jean, jumping up and down excitedly.

"I'm sure it had something to do with it anyway," said Betty.

"Why don't we name it Petunia?" cried Albert.

"Of course!" cried Betty. "The very thing!"

"And we can call it Pet for short," Albert added, stroking the rabbit's soft ears.

On their way home, Albert and Betty stopped at Grandma Kuller's house to show her their treasure.

"It's all because you helped us make those Easter eggs, Grandma Kuller," said Betty happily.

"There wasn't another basket anything like ours, the judges said," added Albert proudly.

"And I helped you with the eggs, my dears," said Grandma Kuller, "because I was quite sure that you had a very good reason for spending the money you had been saving for something besides dyes. And today, from what Mr. Hicks told me, I put two and two together and made it 'Pink Petunias.'"

Fairy and Folk Tales

The Apple of Contentment

From *Pepper and Salt,* by Howard Pyle.

14 minutes

There was a woman once, and she had three daughters. The first daughter squinted with both eyes, yet the woman loved her as she loved salt, for she herself squinted with both eyes. The second daughter had one shoulder higher than the other, and eyebrows as black as soot in the chimney, yet the woman loved her as well as she loved the other, for she herself had black eyebrows and one shoulder higher than the other. The youngest daughter was as pretty as a ripe apple, and had hair as fine as silk and the color of pure gold, but the woman loved her not at all, for, as I have said, she herself was neither pretty, nor had she hair the color of pure gold.

The first sister and the second sister dressed in their Sunday clothes every day, and sat in the sun doing nothing, just as though they had been born ladies, both of them.

As for Christine—that was the name of the youngest girl—she dressed in nothing but rags, and had to drive the geese to the hills in the morning and home again in the evening, so that they might feed on the young grass all day and grow fat.

The first sister and the second sister had white bread (and butter besides) and as much fresh milk as they could drink; but Christine had to eat cheese parings and bread crumbs, and had hardly enough of them to keep Goodman Hunger from whispering in her ear.

Well, one morning Christine started off to the hills with her flock of geese, and in her hands she carried her knitting, at which she worked to save time. So she went along the dusty road until, by-and-by, she came to a place where a bridge crossed the brook, and what should she see there but a little red cap, with a silver bell at the point of it, hanging from an alder branch. It was such a nice, pretty little red cap that Christine thought that she would take it home with her, for she had never seen the like of it in all of her life before. So she put it in her pocket, and then off she went with her geese again. But she had hardly gone two score of paces when she heard a voice calling her, "Christine! Christine!"

She looked, and whom should she see but a queer little gray man, with a great head as big as a cabbage and little legs as thin as young radishes.

"What do you want?" said Christine. Oh, the little man only wanted his cap again, for without it, he could not go back home into the hill where he belonged.

But how did the cap come to be hanging from the bush? Christine would like to know that before she gave it back again. Well, the little hill man was fishing by the brook over yonder when a puff of wind blew his cap into the water, and he just hung it up to dry. That was all there was about it; and now would Christine please give it to him?

Christine did not know about that; perhaps she would and perhaps she would not. It was a nice pretty little cap; what would the little underground man give her for it? That was the question.

Oh, the little man would give her five thalers for it, and gladly.

No, five thalers was not enough for such a pretty little cap—see, there was a silver bell hanging to it, too.

Well, the little man did not want to be hard at a bargain; he would give her a hundred thalers for it. No, Christine did not care for money. What else would he give for this nice, dear little cap?

"See, Christine," said the little man, "I will give you this for the cap," and he showed her something in his hand that looked just like a bean, only it was as black as a lump of coal.

"Yes, good; but what is that?" said Christine.

"That," said the little man, "is a seed from the apple of contentment. Plant it, and from it will grow a tree, and from the tree an apple. Everybody in the world that sees the apple will long for it, but nobody in the world can pluck it but you. It will always be meat and drink to you when you are hungry, and warm clothes to your back when you are cold. Moreover, as soon as you pluck it from the tree, another as good will grow in its place. Now, will you give me my hat?"

Oh, yes; Christine would give the little man his cap for such a seed as that, and gladly enough. So the little man gave Christine the seed and Christine gave the little man his cap again. He put the cap on his head, and puff! away he was gone.

So Christine took the seed home with her, and planted it before the window of her room. The next morning when she looked out of the window, she beheld a beautiful tree, and on the tree hung an apple that shone in the sun as though it were pure gold. Then she plucked the apple as easily as though it were a gooseberry, and as soon as she had plucked it another as good grew in its place. Being hungry, she ate it, and thought that she had never eaten anything as good, for it tasted like a pancake with honey and milk.

By-and-by the oldest sister came out of the house and looked around, and when she saw the beautiful tree with the golden apple hanging from it you can guess how she stared.

Presently she began to long and long for the apple. "I will just pluck it," she said, "and no one will be the wiser for it." But that was easier said than done. She

79

reached and reached, but she might as well have reached for the moon; she climbed and climbed, but she might as well have climbed for the sun—for either one would have been as easy to get as that which she wanted. At last she had to give up trying for it, and her temper was none the sweeter for that, you may be sure.

After a while came the second sister, and when she saw the golden apple, she wanted it just as much as the first had done, but she was no more able to get it than the other had been.

Last of all came the mother, and she also strove to pluck the apple. But it was no use. She had no more luck of her trying than her daughters; all that the three could do was to stand under the tree and look at the apple, and wish for it.

As for Christine, she had nothing to do but to pluck an apple whenever she wanted it. Was she hungry? There was the apple hanging on the tree for her. Was she thirsty? There was the apple. Cold? There was the apple. So you see, she was the happiest girl alive.

. . . . .

One day, a king came riding along the road, and all of his people with him. He looked up and saw the apple hanging on the tree, and a great desire came upon him to have a taste of it. So he called one of the servants to him, and told him to go and ask whether it could be bought for a potful of gold. So the servant went to the house, and knocked on the door—rap! tap! tap!

"What do you want?" said the mother of the three sisters, coming to the door.

Oh, nothing much; only a king was out there in the road, and wanted to know if she would sell the apple yonder for a potful of gold.

Yes, the woman would do that. Just pay her the pot of gold and he might go and pluck it and welcome. So the servant gave her the gold, and then he tried to pluck

80

the apple. First he reached for it, and then he climbed for it, and then he shook the limb. But it was no use for him to try; he could not get it.

At last the servant had to go back to the king. The apple was there he said, and the woman had sold it, but try and try as he would, he could no more get it than he could get the little stars in the sky.

Then the king told the steward to go and get it for him; but the steward, though he was a tall man and a strong man, could no more pluck the apple than the servant. So he had to go back to the king with an empty fist. No, he could not gather it either.

Then the king went himself. He knew he could pluck it —of course he could! Well, he tried and tried, but nothing came of his trying, and he had to ride away at last without having had so much as a smell of the apple.

After the king came home, he talked and dreamed and thought of nothing but the apple. At last he grew melancholy and sick for want of that which he could not get. So he sent for the wise man, who told him that the only one who could pluck the fruit of contentment for him was the one to whom the tree belonged. This was one of the daughters of the woman who had sold the apple to him for a pot of gold.

When the king heard this, he was very glad; he had his horse saddled and he and his court rode away, and came at last to the cottage where Christine lived. There they found the mother and the elder sisters, for Christine was away on the hills with her geese.

The king took off his hat and made a fine bow. The wise man at home had told him this and that; now to which one of her daughters did the apple tree belong? So asked the king.

"Oh, it is my oldest daughter who owns the tree," said the woman.

81

Then if the oldest daughter would pluck the apple for him, he would take her home and marry her and make a queen of her. Only let her get it for him without delay.

Prut! that would never do. What! was the girl to climb the apple tree before the king and all of the court? No! Let the king go home and she would bring the apple to him all in good time; that was what the woman said.

Well, the king would do that, only let her make haste, for he wanted the apple very much indeed.

As soon as the king had gone, the woman and her daughters sent for the goose-girl. They told her that the king wanted the apple yonder, and that she must pluck it for her sister to take to him; if she did not do this, they said they would throw her into the well. So Christine had to pluck the fruit; and as soon as she had done so, the oldest sister wrapped it up in a napkin and set off with it to the king's house. Rap! tap! tap! she knocked at the door. Had she brought the apple for the king? Oh, yes, she had brought it. Here it was, all wrapped up in a fine napkin.

As soon as she had come before the king, she opened her napkin. There was nothing in it but a hard round stone! When the king saw only a stone, he was so angry that he told them to put the girl out of the house.

Then the king sent his steward to the house where Christine and her sisters lived. He told the woman that he had come to find whether she had any other daughters.

Yes, the woman had another daughter, and, to tell the truth, it was she who owned the tree. Just let the steward go home again and the girl would fetch the apple in a little while.

As soon as the steward had gone, they sent to the hills for Christine again. Look! she must pluck the apple for the second sister to take to the king. If she did not, they would throw her into the well.

So Christine had to pluck it and give it to the second sister, who wrapped it up in a napkin and set off for the king's house. But she fared no better than the other, for when she opened the napkin, there was nothing in it but a lump of mud. So they packed her off home with her apron to her eyes.

After a while, the king's steward came to the house again. Had the woman no other daughter than these two?

Well, yes, there was one, but she was a poor ragged thing, of no account, and fit for nothing in the world but to tend the geese.

Where was she?

Oh, she was up on the hills now tending her flock.

But could the steward see her?

Yes, he might see her, but she was nothing but a poor simpleton.

That was all very good, but the steward would like to see her, for that was what the king had sent him there for.

So there was nothing to do but to send to the hills for Christine.

After a while she came and the steward asked her if she could pluck the apple yonder for the king.

Yes; Christine could do that easily enough. So she reached and picked it as though it had been nothing but a gooseberry on a bush. Then the steward took off his hat and made her a low bow in spite of her ragged dress, for he saw that she was the one for whom they had been looking all this time.

So Christine slipped the golden apple into her pocket, and then she and the steward set off to the king's palace together.

When they had come there everybody began to titter and laugh to see what a poor ragged goose-girl the steward had brought home with him. But for that he cared not a rap.

"Have you brought the apple?" said the king, as soon as Christine had come before him.

Yes; here it was; and Christine thrust her hand into her pocket and brought it forth. Then the king took a great bite of it, and as soon as he had done so he looked at Christine and thought that he had never seen such a pretty girl. As for her rags, he minded them no more than one minds the spots on a cherry; that was because he had eaten of the apple of contentment.

And were they married? Of course they were! And a grand wedding it was, I can tell you. Christine's mother and sisters were there, and, what is more, they danced with the others, though I believe they would rather have danced upon pins and needles.

"Never mind," said they. "We still have the apple of contentment at home, though we cannot taste of it." But no; they had nothing of the kind. The next morning, it stood before the young Queen Christine's window, just as it had at her old home, for it belonged to her and to no one else in the world. That was lucky for the king, for he needed a taste of it now and then as much as anybody else, and no one could pluck it for him but Christine.

The Brave Little Tailor

From *Fairy Tales,* by J. L. K. Grimm and W. K.
Grimm.   17 minutes

One summer morning a little tailor was sitting on his
bench near the window, and working cheerfully with all
his might, when an old woman came down the street
crying:

"Good jelly to sell! Good jelly to sell!"

The cry sounded pleasant in the little tailor's ears, so
he put his head out of the window, and called out, "Here,
my good woman—come here, if you want a customer."

So the poor woman climbed the steps with her heavy
basket, and was obliged to unpack and display all her pots
to the tailor. He looked at every one of them, and lifting
the lids, applied his nose to each, and said at last:

"The jelly seems pretty good; you may weigh me out
four half ounces, or I don't mind having a quarter of a
pound."

The woman, who had expected to find a good customer,
gave him what he asked for, but went off angry and
grumbling.

"This jelly is the very thing for me," cried the little
tailor. "It will give me strength and cunning." And he
took down the bread from the cupboard, cut a whole round
of the loaf, and spread the jelly on it, laid it near him,
and went on stitching more gallantly than ever. All the
while, the scent of the sweet jelly was spreading throughout the room, where there were quantities of flies, so that
soon a regular swarm of them had settled on the bread.

"Now, then, who invited you?" said the tailor, and
drove the unbidden guests away. Then the tailor, not being

able to stand it any longer, took from his chimney-corner
a ragged cloth, and said,

"Now I'll let you have it!" and he beat it among them
unmercifully. When he ceased, and counted the slain, he
found seven lying dead before him.

"What a desperate fellow I am!" he said, wondering
at his own gallantry. "The whole town shall know this."

So he hastened to cut out a belt, and he stitched it,
and put on it in large capitals, "Seven at one blow!"

"—The town, did I say!" said the little tailor. "The
whole world shall know it!"

The tailor fastened the belt around him, and began to
think of going out into the world. So he looked about
in all the house for something that would be useful to
take with him, but he found nothing but some cheese,
which he put in his pocket. Outside the door he noticed
that a bird had got caught in the bushes, so he took that
and put it in his pocket with the cheese. Then he set out
on his way, and as he was light and active, he never felt
tired. The way led over a mountain, and when he reached
the topmost peak he saw a terrible giant sitting there. The
tailor went bravely up to him, called out and said,

"Comrade, good day! I am on the way to seek my
fortune, have you a fancy to go with me?"

The giant looked at the tailor, and said, "You little
rascal! You miserable fellow!"

"That may be!" answered the little tailor, and undoing
his coat he showed the giant his belt. "You can read
there whether I am a man or not!"

The giant read, "Seven at one blow!" and thinking it
meant men that the tailor had killed, felt at once more
respect for the little fellow. But as he wanted to test him,
he took up a stone and squeezed it so hard that water came
out of it.

"Now you do that," said the giant, "—that is, if you
have the strength for it."

"That's not much," said the little tailor. "I call that play," and he put his hand in his pocket and took out the cheese and squeezed it, so that the whey ran out of it.

"Well," said he, "what do you think of that?"

The giant did not know what to say to it, for he could not have believed it of the little man. Then the giant took up a stone and threw it so high that it was nearly out of sight.

"Now, little fellow suppose you do that!"

"Well thrown," said the tailor, "but the stone fell back to earth again—I will throw you one that will never come back." So he felt in his pocket, took out the bird, and threw it into the air. And the bird, when it found itself at liberty, took wing, flew off, and returned no more.

"What do you think of that, comrade?" asked the tailor.

"There is no doubt that you can throw," said the giant, "but we will see if you can carry."

He led the little tailor to a mighty oak tree which had been felled and was lying on the ground, and said, "Now, if you are strong enough, help me to carry this tree out of the wood."

"Willingly," answered the little man. "You take the trunk on your shoulders; I will take the branches with all their foliage, that is much the most difficult."

So the giant took the trunk on his shoulders, and the tailor seated himself on a branch, and the giant, who could not see what he was doing, had the whole tree to carry, and the little man as well. And the little man was very cheerful and merry, and whistled the tune: "There were three tailors riding by," as if carrying the tree was mere child's play. The giant, when he had struggled on under his heavy load a part of the way, was tired out, and cried, "Look here, I must let go the tree!"

The tailor jumped off quickly, and taking hold of the tree with both arms, as if he were carrying it, said to the giant, "You see you can't carry the tree though you are such a big fellow!"

They went on together a little farther, and presently they came to a cherry tree, and the giant took hold of the topmost branches, where the ripest fruit hung, and pulling them downwards, gave them to the tailor to hold, bidding him to eat. But the little tailor was much too weak to hold the tree, and as the giant let go, the tree sprang back, and the tailor was caught up into the air. And when he dropped down again without any damage, the giant said to him,

"How is this? Haven't you strength enough to hold such a weak sprig as that?"

"It is not strength that is lacking," answered the little tailor. "How should it be to one who has slain seven at one blow! I just jumped over the tree because the hunters are shooting down there in the bushes. You jump it too, if you can."

The giant made the attempt, and not being able to vault the tree, he remained hanging in the branches, so that once more the little tailor got the better of him.

Then said the giant, "As you are such a gallant fellow, suppose you come with me to our den, and stay the night."

The tailor was quite willing and followed him. When they reached the den there sat some other giants by the fire, and all gladly welcomed him.

And the giant showed him a bed, and told him he had better lie down upon it and go to sleep. The bed was, however, too big for the tailor, so he did not stay in it, but crept into a corner to sleep. At midnight, the giant got up, took a great staff of iron and beat the bed through with one stroke, and supposed he had made an end of that grasshopper of a tailor. Very early in the morning the giants went into the wood and forgot all about the little tailor, and when they saw him coming after them alive

88

and merry, they were terribly frightened, and, thinking he was going to kill them, they ran away in all haste.

So the little tailor marched on, always following his nose. And after he had gone a great way he entered a courtyard belonging to a king's palace, and there he felt so overpowered with fatigue that he lay down and fell asleep. In the meanwhile various people came, who looked at him very curiously, and read on his belt, "Seven at one blow!"

"Oh!" said they, "why should this great lord come here in time of peace? What a mighty champion he must be."

Then they went and told the king about him, and they thought that if war should break out, what a worthy and useful man he would be, and that he ought not to be allowed to depart at any price. The king then summoned his council, and sent one of his courtiers to the little tailor to beg him, as soon as he should wake up, to consent to serve in the king's army. So the messenger stood and waited at the sleeper's side until his limbs began to stretch, and his eyes to open, and then he gave the tailor the king's message.

"That was the very reason I came," said the little tailor. "I am ready to enter the king's service."

So he was received into it very honorably, and given a special house of his own to live in. But the rest of the soldiers were very much set against the little tailor.

"What shall be done about it?" they said among themselves. "If we pick a quarrel and fight with him then seven of us will fall at each blow."

So they came to a resolution, and went all together to the king to ask for their discharge.

"We never intended," said they, "to serve with a man who kills seven at a blow."

The king felt sorry to lose all his faithful servants because of one man, but he did not dare to dismiss the little tailor for fear he should kill all the king's people, and place himself upon the throne. He thought a long while about it, and at last made up his mind what to do. He sent for the little tailor, and told him that as he was so great a warrior he had a proposal to make to him. He said that in a wood in his dominions dwelt two giants, who did great damage by robbery, murder, and fire, and that no man durst go near them for fear of his life. But that if the tailor should overcome and slay both these giants the king would give him his only daughter in marriage, and half his kingdom as dowry, and that a hundred horsemen should go with him to give him assistance.

"That would be something for a man like me!" thought the little tailor. "A beautiful princess and half a kingdom are not to be had every day." And he said to the King, "Oh, yes, I can soon overcome the giants, and yet have no need of the hundred horsemen; he who can kill seven at one blow has no need to be afraid of two."

So the little tailor set out, and the hundred horsemen followed him. When he came to the border of the wood he said to his escort, "Stay here while I go to attack the giants."

Then he sprang into the wood, and looked about him right and left. After a while he caught sight of the two giants; they were lying down under a tree asleep, and snoring so that all the branches shook. The little tailor, filled both his pockets with stones and climbed up into the tree, and made his way to an overhanging bough, so that he could seat himself just above the sleepers; and from there he let one stone after another fall on the chest of one of the giants. For a long time the giant was quite unaware of this, but at last he woke up and pushed his comrade, and said:

"What are you hitting me for?"

"You are dreaming," said the other. "I am not touching you." When they again went to sleep, the tailor let fall a stone on the other giant. "What can that be?" cried he. "What are you casting at me?"

90

"I am casting nothing at you," answered the first, grumbling.

They quarreled about it for a while, but as they were tired, they gave it up at last, and their eyes closed once more. Then the little tailor began his game anew, picked out a heavier stone and threw it down with force upon the first giant's chest.

"This is too much!" cried he, and sprang up like a madman and struck his companion such a blow that the tree shook above them. They fought with such fury that they tore up trees by their roots to use for weapons against each other, so that at last both of them lay dead upon the ground. And now the little tailor got down.

Then he drew his sword and gave each of the giants a few hacks in the breast, and went back to the horsemen and said. "The deed is done, I have made an end of both of them; but it went hard with me; in the struggle they rooted up trees to defend themselves, but it was of no use, they had to fight with a man who can kill seven at one blow."

"Then you are not wounded?" asked the horsemen.

"Nothing of the sort!" answered the tailor, "I have not turned a hair."

The horsemen still would not believe it, and rode into the wood to see for themselves and there they found the giants and all about them the uprooted trees.

The little tailor then claimed the promised boon, but the king repented of his offer, and he sought again how to rid himself of the hero.

"Before you can possess my daughter and the half of my kingdom," said he to the tailor, "you must perform another heroic act. In the wood lives a unicorn who does great damage; you must secure him."

"A unicorn does not strike more terror into me than two giants. Seven at one blow!—that is my way," was the tailor's answer.

So, taking a rope and ax with him, he went out into the wood, and told those who were ordered to attend him to wait outside. The unicorn soon came out and sprang at him, as if he would make an end of him without delay. "Softly, softly," said he, "most haste, worst speed," and remained standing until the animal came quite near, then he slipped quietly behind a tree. The unicorn ran with all his might against the tree and stuck his horn so deep into the trunk that he could not get it out again, and so was taken.

"Now I have you," said the tailor, coming out from behind the tree, and, putting the rope round the unicorn's neck, he took the ax, set free the horn, and when all his party were assembled he led forth the animal and brought it to the king.

The king did not yet wish to give him the promised reward, and set him a third task to do. Before the wedding could take place, the tailor was to secure a wild boar which had done a great deal of damage in the wood. The huntsmen were to accompany him.

"All right," said the tailor, "this is child's play."

But he did not take the huntsmen into the wood, and they were all the better pleased, for the wild boar had many a time before received them in such a way that they had no fancy to disturb him. When the boar caught sight of the tailor he ran at him with foaming mouth and gleaming tusks to bear him to the ground, but the nimble hero rushed into a chapel which chanced to be near, and jumped quickly out of a window on the other side. The boar ran after him and when he got inside, the door shut behind him, and there he was imprisoned, for the creature was too big to jump out of the window too. Then the little tailor called the huntsmen that they might see the prisoner with their own eyes; and then he betook himself to the king, who now, whether he liked it or not, was obliged to fulfill his promise, and give him his daughter and the half of his kingdom. But if he had known that the great warrior was only a little tailor he would have taken it still more amiss. So the wedding was celebrated with great splendor and the tailor was made into a king.

One night the young queen heard her husband talking in his sleep and saying, "Now, boy, make me that waistcoat and patch me those breeches or I will lay my yard measure about your shoulders."

And so, as she perceived of what low birth her husband was, she went to her father the next morning and told him all, and begged him to set her free from a man who was nothing better than a tailor. The king bade her be comforted, saying,

"Tonight leave your bedroom door open; my guard shall stand outside, and when he is asleep, they shall come in and bind him and carry him off to a ship, and he shall be sent to the other side of the world."

So the wife felt consoled, but the king's water bearer, who had been listening all the while, went to the little tailor and disclosed to him the whole plan.

"I shall put a stop to this," said he.

So at night, he lay down as usual in bed, and when his wife thought he was asleep, she got up, opened the door and lay down again. The little tailor, who only made believe to be asleep, began to murmur plainly.

"Now, boy, make me that waistcoat and patch me those breeches, or I will lay my yard measure about your shoulders! I have slain seven at one blow, killed two giants, caught a unicorn, and taken a wild boar, and shall I be afraid of those who are standing outside my room door?"

And when they heard the tailor say this, a great fear seized them. They fled away as if they had been wild hares, and none of them would venture to attack him.

And so the little tailor all his lifetime remained a king.

The Giant Who Had No Heart in His Body

From *Popular Tales from the Norse,* by Peter
Christen Asbjörnsen and Jörgen Engebretsen Moe.
Translated by Sir George Webbe Dasent.   13 minutes

Once upon a time there was a king who had seven sons,
and he loved them so much that he could never bear to be
without them all at once, but one must always be with him.
Now, when they were grown up, six were to set off to woo,
but as for the youngest, his father kept him at home, and
the others were to bring back a princess for him to the
palace. So the king gave the six the finest clothes you ever
set eyes on, and each had his horse, which cost many,
many hundred dollars, and they set off. Now, when they
had been to many palaces, and seen many princesses, at
last they came to a king who had six daughters; such lovely
king's daughters they had never seen, and so they fell to
wooing them, each one, and when they had got them for
sweethearts, they set off home again, but they quite forgot
that they were to bring back with them a sweetheart for
their brother, who stayed at home, for they were over head
and ears in love.

But when they had gone a good bit on their way, they
passed close by a steep hillside, like a wall, where a giant's
house was, and there the giant came out, and set his eyes
upon them, and turned them all into stone, princes and
princesses and all. Now the king waited and waited for
his six sons, but the more he waited the longer they stayed
away; so he fell into great sorrow, and said he should
never know what it was to be glad again.

"And if I didn't have you," he said to his youngest son, "I would live no longer, so full of sorrow am I for the loss of your brothers."

"Well, but now I've been thinking to ask your leave to set out and find them again; that's what I'm thinking of," said the prince.

"Nay, nay!" said his father, "that leave you shall never get, for then you would stay away, too."

But he had set his heart upon it; go he would; and he begged and prayed so long that the king was forced to let him go. Now, you must know the king had no other horse to give the prince but an old broken-down jade, for his six other sons and their train had taken all his horses; but the prince did not care a pin for that, he sprang upon his sorry old steed.

"Farewell, father," said he, "I'll come back, never fear, and like enough I shall bring my six brothers back with me," and with that he rode off.

When he had ridden a while, he came to a raven which lay in the road and flapped its wings and was not able to get out of the way, it was so starved.

"Oh, dear friend," said the raven, "give me a little food, and I'll help you again at your utmost need."

"I haven't much food," said the prince, "and I don't see how you'll ever be able to help me much; but still I can spare you a little. I see you need it."

So he gave the raven some of the food he had brought with him.

Now, when he had gone a bit further, he came to a brook, and in the brook lay a great salmon which had got upon a dry place and dashed itself about and could not get into the water again.

"Oh, dear friend," said the salmon to the prince, "shove me out into the water, and I'll help you at your utmost need."

"Well!" said the prince, "the help you'll give me will not be great, I daresay, but it's a pity you should lie there and choke," and with that he shoved the fish out into the stream again.

After that he went a long, long way, and there met a wolf which was so famished that it lay and crawled along the road on its belly.

"Dear friend, do let me have your horse," said the wolf. "I'm so hungry the wind whistles through my ribs; I've had nothing to eat these two years."

"No," said the prince, "this will never do; first I came to a raven, and I was forced to give him my food; next I came to a salmon, and I had to help him into the water again; and now you will have my horse. It can't be done, that it can't, for then I should have nothing to ride on."

"Nay, dear friend, but I can help you," said the wolf, "you can ride upon my back, and I'll help you again in your utmost need."

"Well! the help I shall get from you will not be great, I'll be bound," said the prince, "but you may take my horse, since you are in such need."

So, when the wolf had eaten the horse, the prince took the bit and put it into the wolf's mouth, and laid the saddle on his back; and now the wolf was so strong, after what he had got inside, that he set off with the prince like nothing. He had never ridden so fast before.

"When we have gone a bit farther," said the wolf, "I'll show you the giant's house."

So after a while they came to it.

"See, here is the giant's house," said the wolf, "and here are your six brothers, whom the giant has turned into stone; and here are their six brides, and away yonder is the door, and in that door you must go."

"Nay, but I daren't go in," said the prince, "he'll take my life."

"No! no!" said the wolf, "when you get in you'll find a princess, and she'll tell you what to do to make an end of the giant. Only mind and do as she bids you."

Well, the prince went in, but, truth to say, he was very much afraid. But the giant was away, and in one of the rooms sat the princess, just as the wolf had said, and so lovely a princess he had never yet set eyes on.

"Oh! heaven help you! whence have you come!" said the princess, as she saw him. "It will surely be your death. No one can make an end of the giant who lives here, for he has no heart in his body."

"Well! well!" said the prince, "but now that I am here, I may as well try what I can do with him; and I will see if I can't free my brothers, who are standing turned to stone out of doors; and you, too, I will try to save, that I will."

"Well, if you must, you must," said the princess, "and so let us see if we can't hit on a plan. Just creep under the bed yonder, and mind and listen to what he and I talk about. But, pray, do lie as still as a mouse."

So he crept under the bed, and he had scarce got well underneath it, before the giant came home.

"Ha!" roared the giant, "what a smell of Christian blood there is in the house!"

"Yes, I know there is," said the princess, "for there came a magpie flying with a man's bone, and let it fall down the chimney. I made all the haste I could to get it out, but the odor doesn't go off so soon."

So the giant said no more about it, and when night came, they went to bed. After a while, the princess said, "There is one thing I'd be so glad to ask you about, if I only dared."

"What thing is that?" asked the giant.

"Only where is it you keep your heart, since you don't carry it about with you?" said the princess.

97

"Ah! that's a thing you've no business to ask about; but if you must know, it lies under the door sill," said the giant.

"Ho! ho!" said the prince to himself under the bed, "then we'll soon see if we can't find it."

Next morning the giant got up early, and strode off to the wood; but he was hardly out of the house before the prince and the princess set to work to look under the door sill for his heart; but the more they dug, and the more they hunted, the more they couldn't find it.

"He has balked us this time," said the princess, "but we'll try him once more."

So she picked all the prettiest flowers she could find, and strewed them over the door sill, which they had laid in its right place again; and when the time came for the giant to come home, the prince crept under the bed. Just as he was well under, back came the giant.

Snuff—snuff, went the giant's nose. "My eyes and limbs, what a smell of Christian blood there is in here," he said.

"I know there is," said the princess, "for there came a magpie flying with a man's bone in his bill, and let it fall down the chimney. I made as much haste as I could to get it out, but I daresay it's that you smell."

So the giant held his peace, and said no more about it. A little while after, he asked who it was that had strewed flowers about the door sill.

"Oh, I, of course," said the princess.

"And pray, what's the meaning of all this?" said the giant.

"Ah!" said the princess, "I'm so fond of you that I couldn't help strewing them, when I knew that your heart lay under there."

"You don't say so," said the giant, "but after all it doesn't lie there at all."

So when they went to bed, the princess asked the giant again where his heart was, for she said she would so like to know.

"Well," said the giant, "if you must know, it lies away yonder in the cupboard against the wall."

"So, so!" thought the prince and the princess, "then we'll soon try to find it."

Next morning the giant was away early, and strode off in the wood, and as soon as he was gone the prince and the princess were in the cupboard hunting for his heart, but the more they sought for it, the less they found it.

"Well," said the princess, "we'll just try him once more."

So she decked out the cupboard with flowers and garlands, and when the time came for the giant to come home, the prince crept under the bed again.

Then back came the giant.

Snuff—snuff! "My eyes and limbs, what a smell of Christian blood there is in here!"

"I know there is," said the princess, "for a little while since there came a magpie flying with a man's bone in his bill, and let it fall down the chimney. I made all the haste I could to get it out of the house again; but after all my pains, I daresay it's that you smell."

When the giant heard that, he said no more about it; but a little while after, he saw the cupboard was all decked about with flowers and garlands; so he asked who it was that had done that? Who could it be but the princess?

"And, pray, what's the meaning of all this tomfoolery?" asked the giant.

"Oh, I'm so fond of you, I couldn't help doing it when I knew that your heart lay there," said the princess.

"How can you be so silly as to believe any such thing?" said the giant.

"Oh, but how can I help believing it, when you say it?" said the princess.

"You're a goose," said the giant, "where my heart is, you will never come."

"Well," said the princess, "but for all that, 'twould be such a pleasure to know where it really lies."

Then the poor giant could hold out no longer, but was forced to say,

"Far, far away in a lake lies an island; on that island stands a church; in that church is a well; in that well swims a duck; in that duck there is an egg, and in that egg there lies my heart—you darling!"

In the morning early, while it was still gray dawn, the giant strode off to the wood.

"Yes! now I must set off, too," said the prince "if I only knew how to find the way." He took a long, long farewell of the princess, and when he got out of the giant's door, there stood the wolf waiting for him. So the prince told him all that had happened inside the house, and said now he wished to ride to the well in the church, if he only knew the way. So the wolf bade him jump on his back, he'd soon find the way; and away they went, till the wind whistled after them, over hill and dale. After they had travelled many, many days, they came at last to the lake. Then the prince did not know how to get over it, but the wolf bade him not to be afraid, but stick on, and so he jumped into the lake with the prince on his back, and swam over to the island. So they came to the church; but the church keys hung high, high up on the top of the tower, and at first the prince did not know how to get them down.

"You must call on the raven," said the wolf.

So the prince called on the raven, and in a trice the raven came, and flew up and fetched the keys, and so the prince got into the church. But when he came to the well, there was the duck, swimming about backwards and forwards, just as the giant had said. So the prince stood and coaxed it and coaxed it, till it came to him, and he grasped it in his hand; but just as he lifted it up from the water the duck dropped the egg into the well, and he was beside himself to know how to get it out again.

"Well, now you must call on the salmon, to be sure," said the wolf; and the king's son called on the salmon, and the salmon came and fetched up the egg from the bottom of the well.

Then the wolf told him to squeeze the egg, and as soon as ever he squeezed it the giant screamed out.

"Squeeze it again," said the wolf; and when the prince did so, the giant screamed more piteously, and begged and prayed so prettily to be spared, saying he would do all that the prince wished if he would only not squeeze his heart in two.

"Tell him, if he will restore to life again your six brothers and their brides, whom he has turned to stone, you will spare his life," said the wolf. Yes, the giant was ready to do that, and he turned the six brothers into king's sons again, and their brides into king's daughters.

Now, the prince rode back again on the wolf to the giant's house, and there stood all his six brothers alive and merry, with their brides. Then he went into the hillside after his bride, and so they all set off home again to their father's house. And you may fancy how glad the old king was when he saw all his seven sons come back, each with his bride.

"But the loveliest bride of all is the bride of the youngest," said the king, "and he shall sit uppermost at the table, with her by his side."

So he sent out and called a great wedding feast, and the mirth was both loud and long; and if they have not done feasting, why, they are still at it.

How Boots Befooled the King

From *The Wonder Clock,* by Howard Pyle.

15 minutes

Once upon a time there was a king who was the wisest in all of the world. So wise was he that no one had ever befooled him, which is a rare thing, I can tell you. Now, this king had a daughter who was as pretty as a ripe apple, so that there was no end to the number of the lads who came asking to marry her. Every day there were two or three of them dawdling round the house, so that at last the old king grew tired of having them always about.

So he sent word far and near that whoever should befool him might have the princess and half of the kingdom to boot, for he thought that it would be a wise man indeed who could trick him. But the king also said, that whoever should try to befool him and should fail, should have a good whipping. This was to keep all foolish fellows away.

The princess was so pretty that there was no lack of lads who came to have a try for her and half of the kingdom, but every one of them went away with a sore back and no luck.

Now, there was a man who was well off in the world, and who had three sons; the first was named Peter, and the second was named Paul. Peter and Paul thought themselves as wise as anybody in all the world, and their father thought as they did.

As for the youngest son, he was called Boots. Nobody thought anything of him except that he was silly, for he did nothing but sit poking in the warm ashes all of the day.

One morning Peter spoke up and said that he was going to the town to have a try at befooling the king, for it would be a fine thing to have a princess in the family. His father did not say no, for if anybody was wise enough to befool the king, Peter was the lad.

So, after Peter had eaten a good breakfast, off he set for the town, right foot foremost. After a while he came to the king's house and rap! tap! tap! he knocked at the door.

Well, what did he want? Oh! he would only like to have a try at befooling the king.

Very good; he should have his try. He was not the first one who had been there that morning, early as it was.

So Peter was shown in to the king.

"Oh, look!" said he, "yonder are three black geese out in the courtyard!"

But no, the king was not to be fooled so easily as all that. "One goose is enough to look at at a time," said he. "Take him away and give him a whipping!"

And so they did, and Peter went home bleating like a sheep.

One day Paul spoke up. "I should like to go and have a try for the princess, too," said he.

Well, his father did not say no, for, after all, Paul was the more clever of the two.

So off Paul went as merrily as a duck in the rain. By and by he came to the castle, and then he too was brought before the king just as Peter had been.

"Oh, look!" said he, "yonder is a crow sitting in the tree with three white stripes on his back!"

But the king was not so silly as to be fooled in that way. "Here is a Jack," said he, "who will soon have more stripes on his back than he will like. Take him away and give him his whipping!"

Then it was done as the king had said, and Paul went away home bawling like a calf.

One day, up spoke Boots. "I should like to go and have a try for the pretty princess, too," said he.

At this, they all stared and sniggered. What! he go where his clever brothers had failed, and had nothing to show for the trying but a good beating? What had come over the lout! Here was a pretty business, to be sure! That was what they all said.

But all of this rolled away from Boots like water from a duck's back. No matter, he would like to go and have a try like the others. So he begged and begged until his father was glad to let him go to be rid of his teasing, if nothing else.

Then Boots asked if he might have the old tattered hat that hung back of the chimney. Oh, yes, he might have that if he wanted it, for nobody with good wits was likely to wear such a thing.

So Boots took the hat, and after he had brushed the ashes from his shoes, set off for the town, whistling as he went.

The first body whom he met was an old woman with a great load of earthenware pots and crocks on her shoulders.

"Good day, mother," said Boots. "Good day, son," said she.

"What will you take for all of your pots and crocks?" said Boots.

"Three shillings," said she.

"I will give you five shillings if you will come and stand in front of the king's house, and do thus and so when I say this and that," said Boots. Oh, yes! she would do that willingly enough.

So Boots and the old woman went on together, and presently came to the king's house. When they had come there, Boots sat down in front of the door and began bawling as loud as he could—"No, I will not! I will not do it, I say. No, I will not do it!"

So he kept on bawling louder and louder, until he made such a noise that, at last, the king himself came out to see what all the hubbub was about. But when Boots saw him, he only bawled out louder than ever, "No, I will not! I will not! I will not do it, I say!"

"Stop! Stop!" cried the king. "What is all this about?"

"Why," said Boots, "everybody wants to buy my cap, but I will not sell it! I will not do it, I say!"

"But why should anybody want to buy such a cap as that?" said the king.

"Because," said Boots, "it is a fooling cap, and the only one in all the world."

"A fooling cap!" said the king. For he did not like to hear of such a cap as that coming into town. "Hum-m-m-m! I should like to see you fool somebody with it. Could you fool that old body yonder with the pots and crocks?"

"Oh, yes! that is easily enough done," said Boots, and without more ado, he took off his tattered cap and blew into it. Then he put it on his head again and bawled out, "Break pots! Break pots!"

No sooner had he spoken these words than the old woman jumped up and began breaking and smashing her pots and crocks as though she had gone crazy. That was what Boots had paid her five shillings for doing, but of it the king knew nothing. "Hui!" said he to himself, "I must buy that hat from that fellow or he will fool the princess away from me for sure and certain." Then he began talking to Boots as sweetly as though he had honey in his mouth. Perhaps Boots would sell the hat to him?

Oh, no! Boots could not think of such a thing as selling his fooling cap. Come, come; the king wanted that hat, and sooner than miss buying it, he would give a whole bag of gold money for it.

At this Boots looked up and looked down, scratching his head. Well, he supposed he would have to sell the hat sometime, and the king might as well have it as anybody else. But for all that, he did not like parting with it.

So the king gave Boots the bag of gold, and Boots gave the king the old tattered hat, and then he went his way.

After Boots had gone, the king blew into the hat and blew into the hat, but though he blew enough breath into it to sail a big ship, he did not befool so much as a single titmouse. Then, at last, he began to see that the fooling cap was good on nobody else's head but Boots'; and he was none too pleased at that, you may be sure.

As for Boots, with his bag of gold he bought the finest clothing to be had in the town, and when the next morning had come, he started away bright and early for the king's house. "I have come," said he, "to marry the princess, if you please."

At this the king hemmed and hawed and scratched his head. Yes; Boots had befooled him sure enough, but after all, he could not give up the princess for such a thing as that. Still, he would give Boots another chance. Now, there was the high councilor, who was the wisest man in all the world. Did Boots think he could fool him also?

Oh, yes! Boots thought it might be done. Very well; if he could befool the high councilor, so as to bring him to the castle the next morning against his will, Boots should have the princess and the half of the kingdom; if he did not do so, he should have his beating.

Then Boots went away, and the king thought that he was rid of him now for good and all.

As for the high councilor, he was not pleased with the matter at all, for he did not like the thought of being fooled by a clever rogue, and taken here and there against his will. So when he had come home, he armed all his servants with blunderbusses and then waited to give Boots a welcome when he should come.

But Boots was not going to fall into any such trap as that! No indeed! Not he! The next morning, he went quietly and bought a fine large meal sack. Then he put a black wig over his beautiful red hair, so that no one might know him. After that he went to the place where the high

106

councilor lived, and when he had come there he crawled inside the sack and lay just beside the door of the house.

By and by, out came one of the maid servants to the door, and there lay the great meal sack with somebody in it.

"Ach!" cried she, "who is there?" But Boots only said, "Sh-h-h-h!"

Then the serving maid went back into the house, and told the high councilor that one lay outside in a great meal sack, and that all he said was "Sh-h-h-h-h!"

So the councilor went himself to see what it was all about. "What do you want here?" said he.

"Sh-h-h-h-h!" said Boots, "I am not to be talked to now. This is a wisdom sack, and I am learning wisdom as fast as a drake can eat peas!"

"And what wisdom have you learned?" said the councilor.

Oh, Boots had learned wisdom about everything in the world. He had learned that the clever scamp who had fooled the king yesterday was coming with seventeen tall men to take the high councilor, willy nilly, to the castle that morning.

When the high councilor heard this, he fell to trembling till his teeth rattled in his head. "And have you learned how I can get the better of this clever scamp?" said he.

Oh yes! Boots had learned that easily enough. So, good! Then if the wise man in the sack would tell the high councilor how to escape the clever rogue, the high councilor would give the wise man twenty dollars. But, no, that was not to be done; wisdom was not bought so cheaply as the high councilor seemed to think.

Well, the councilor would give him a hundred dollars then.

That was good! A hundred dollars was a hundred dollars. If the councilor would give him that much, he might get into the sack himself and then he could learn all the wisdom that he wanted and more besides!

So Boots crawled out of the sack, and the councilor paid his hundred dollars and crawled in.

As soon as he was in all snug and safe, Boots drew the mouth of the sack together, and tied it tightly. Then he flung sack, councilor and all over his shoulder, and started away to the king's house, and anybody who met them could see with half an eye that the councilor was going against his will.

When Boots came to the king's castle, he laid the councilor down in the goose house, and then he went to the king.

When the king saw Boots again, he bit his lips with vexation. "Well," said he, "have you fooled the councilor?"

"Oh, yes!" said Boots, "I have done that."

And where was the councilor now? Oh, Boots had just left him down in the goose house. He was tied up safe and sound in a sack, waiting till the king should send for him.

So the councilor was sent for, and when he came, the king saw at once that he had been brought against his will.

"And now may I marry the princess?" said Boots.

But the king was not willing for him to marry the princess yet; no! no! Boots must not go so fast. There was more to be done yet. If he would come tomorrow morning, he might have the princess and welcome, but he would have to pick her out from among fourscore other maids just like her; did he think that he could do that?

Oh, yes! Boots thought that might be easy enough to do.

So, good! Then come tomorrow; but he must understand that if he failed he should have a good whipping, and be sent packing from the town.

So off went Boots, and the king thought that he was rid of him now, for he had never seen the princess, and how could he pick her out from among eighty others?

But Boots was not going to give up so easily as all that! No, not he! He made a little box, and then he hunted up and down until he had caught a live mouse to put into it.

When the next morning came he started away to the king's house, taking his mouse along with him in the box.

There was the king, standing in the doorway, looking out into the street. When he saw Boots coming towards him, he made a wry face. "What!" said he, "Are you back again?"

Oh, yes! Boots was back again. And now if the princess was ready, he would like to go and find her.

So off they marched to a great room, and there stood eighty-and-one maidens, all as much alike as peas in the same dish.

Boots looked here and there, but, even if he had known the princess, he could not have told her from the others. But he was ready for all that. Before any one knew what he was about, he opened the box, and out ran the little mouse among them all. Then what a screaming and a hub-bub there was! Many looked as though they would have liked to swoon, but only one of them did. As soon as the others saw what had happened they forgot all about the mouse, and ran to her and fell to fanning her and slapping her hands and chafing her temples.

"This is the princess," said Boots.

And so it was.

After that, the king could think of nothing more to set Boots to do, so he let him marry the princess as he had promised, and have half of the kingdom to boot.

That is all of this story.

Only this: It is not always the silliest one that sits kicking his feet in the ashes at home.

King Wichtel the First

From story by Julius Sturm. *St. Nicholas.* April 1879.   12 minutes

"If you only knew what I know!" said a poor laborer's son to his sister many years ago.

"It must be something very important," said she.

But the brother replied, "It is indeed something very important, and, if you knew it, you would jump high as the ceiling for joy."

"Oh, then, tell it to me," said the sister, coaxingly.

The brother smote his breast proudly with his hand, and said, "Tonight I can become a king, if only I will."

The sister laughed outright, and said, "You, in your torn jacket, would make a beautiful king!"

"I shall not wear the old jacket," replied the future king. "I shall have a red mantle embroidered with gold, and a gold crown also; and, sister, if you desire it, you can become a princess, and have a beautiful dress; and when I am seated on my gold throne, you will sit near me on a silver one. We shall live in a gold castle, where we can eat anything we want all day, and where we shall not have to pick up any more dry sticks."

"But how will it all come about?" asked his sister, quite astonished and puzzled. "Our parents are very poor people."

The brother gave a knowing look, and said, "I dreamt last night, that ——"

He got no further, for a shrill laugh interrupted him, and his sister cried, "Oh, then, it is all a dream! Thank you, but I don't care to be a dream princess." She would have

110

run away, but her brother held her by the dress, and spoke eagerly.

"Let me finish," he cried. "The principal thing is yet to be told. What I told you, I saw only in a dream; but this is what happened to me: I woke up; the moon shone into my room, and before my bed stood a little man, who had a long gray beard and a brown face full of wrinkles. He looked at me with clear, bright eyes, and laid his finger on his mouth, as if he would say: 'Now be still! quite still!' Then he asked me in a whisper, if I wished to have the dream come true, and if I would like to be a king, and live with you in a gold castle. I nodded to him, and he went on, 'If you decide to have what you have dreamt really happen, come with your sister to the wood this evening when the moon rises, and wait for me under the great fir tree, of which you know. But remember there is one condition: In the gold castle you must let no tears fall on the floor, for if you do, all is lost, and we gnomes are once more without a king.' You will promise—won't you, sister—not to cry in the gold castle? You always cry easily—right off."

The sister gave her hand upon it that she would not cry, because she wanted so much to be a princess. The children had now decided that they would go to the wood that evening, and wait till the moon rose. Before dusk they slipped unnoticed into the wood, for they feared that their parents, when they came from their work, would keep them at home as it was a Saturday, and there was a great deal to be done about the house. They walked hand in hand, till they came to the great fir tree. Then they sat down on the soft moss, meaning to wait till the moon should rise.

After a while the sister said, "I'm thinking all the time of our parents, and I am so sad that I must cry. May I cry now?"

"Certainly," said the brother, "we are not in the gold castle yet. Cry all you want to, as long as we are in the woods."

111

And the sister cried until she fell asleep with red eyes. The brother sat near her, and his one thought was how nice it would be when once he should be king! At last he, too, got tired and sleepy, and began to nod.

When the brother and sister awoke, they looked around, very much astonished, for they were dressed most beautifully. The brother had on fine black velvet stockings, and a glittering coat of dark blue silk. Around his shoulders hung a red mantle, embroidered with gold, while on his black curly head shone a golden crown. The sister wore a sky-blue dress, dotted with silver stars, and on her blonde hair rested a coronet, sparkling with precious stones.

While they gazed at each other, mute with amazement, the little man with the gray beard stood before them and cried out, "Welcome! welcome! I am right glad you have come."

Then he blew a little silver horn that he wore at his side, and a long train of gray-bearded little men came at the signal. They bore a splendid canopy, and under it a gold sedan chair and a silver one, each resting on glistening poles of ebony. The brother must sit in the gold chair, and the sister in the silver one. Slowly and with pomp the train moved through the woods till it came to a mountain covered with old and stately fir trees. At the foot of this mountain opened a great wide cavern, in which burned numerous lights. This the train entered, and then proceeded further on, through a long passage, till at last it came to a spacious, lofty hall, which was light as day.

In the middle of this vast hall stood a golden castle, much more beautiful than the one the boy had seen in his dream. Here, the brother and sister got down from their chairs, and went, accompanied by the little men, up the steps of rock crystal to the portal of the castle. The door sprang open, and the little men conducted the two into a large hall, in which there were two thrones, one of gold, and one of silver. The feet of the gold throne represented four lions, and on the back of it was a golden eagle with outspread wings. The silver throne was upheld by four silver lilies, and on its back stood a silver swan. The brother sat on the first throne, while the sister sat on the second.

Hardly were they seated when a buzzing sound went through the assembly, and the little men came over to the thrones, and cried with loud voices:

"Long live our king, Wichtel the First!"

At this cry the king rose angrily, and said, "My name is not Wichtel; it is Fritz. Just ask my sister; she knows as well as I."

The sister nodded, but the little man, who had first spoken to the children in the wood, came before the throne, bowed low, and said:

"Pardon me, your majesty, but, if I may be permitted to say it, from this day forth your majesty is no longer Fritz but Wichtel the First, for now you are King of all the Wichtel men."

"If that is so," said King Wichtel, "it shall be my pleasure."

Hardly had he said this, when a little man came before the throne, bearing in his hand a staff with a great knob, and announced that the table was ready.

"I am glad of that," replied King Wichtel, "for I am very hungry."

Thereupon a golden door opened, revealing a long table, set with dainty food. The king and his sister stepped down from their thrones, and took their places at the table; and then the Wichtel men sat down.

The food tasted wonderful; and when the supper was over, one of the Wichtel men led them into an elegant room where there were two beds—one of gold, the other of silver. King Wichtel lay down in the gold bed, and his sister in the silver bed. As they rested on the soft pillows, the brother said:

"Sister, how do you like this gold castle? Is it not very beautiful?"

"Yes, but I wish father and mother were here."

"That is my one wish, too," said the brother. "I wonder what our dear parents are doing now."

"Oh," sighed the sister, "they are looking for us, and when they can't find us they will be anxious, and cry."

"Yes, that they will certainly do, since they loved us so much. When we do not come home, they will think that a wolf has eaten us, just as he ate little Red Ridinghood. You haven't cried yet, sister, have you?"

In a low voice the sister replied, "I have let a few tears fall on the bed, but none on the floor. Do not be angry with me, but I couldn't help crying, for I thought I heard our good mother weeping. You are so still that you, too, must be crying."

"Yes," said a voice from the gold bed, "I thought I heard our good father calling us, and his voice sounded so sad, and so full of anxiety! But I catch all my tears in my hand, so that none can fall on the floor."

Both children wept quietly for a time; at last the sister asked, with a tearful voice, "Will you, then, always be king, and shall we never go back to our parents? That I can never endure; I would rather not be a princess any more, for I should die for longing after them, and then you would be alone in the gold castle."

"Ah!" sighed the brother, "I thought it was much easier and better to be a king, but the gold crown has made my forehead sore, and I would rather pick up dry wood in the forest than always sit on a gold throne; it is so tiresome!"

"Let us each drop a tear on the floor, and then all will be over, and we will go back to our parents," said the sister.

The idea was quite after the brother's liking; so they each let fall a great tear on the floor. Hardly had they done this, when a great cry of lamentation went through the gold castle, and there was a loud crash, and it thundered so fearfully that they both sprang out of bed screaming, and became unconscious.

The castle had disappeared. The children lay as if dead in the great cavern on the cold rock, and around them stood sadly the little Wichtel men. One of them, who had a snow-white beard, and must have been very old, said to the rest:

"Did I not tell you that we could not keep our king this time, any more than on former occasions when we were disappointed? The children of men are all alike. Even the poorest love their parents so much that they long for them, and cry, and this they would do though one should offer them all the magnificence in the whole world."

The Wichtel men bowed their heads sadly, for they would have liked to have had one of the children of men for a king. At last they dressed the children in their old clothes, took them softly out of the hole in the mountain, and laid them under the great fir tree on the soft moss.

When the brother and sister woke up, it was clear day. The sun shone brightly through the green fir branches and the birds sang gayly. The children looked wonderingly at each other; then sprang up rejoicing for they saw their parents, who had been searching for them all night, in the distance. They ran and embraced them and told them of the strange things that had happened to them. But their parents assured them it was all a dream, for there were no Wichtel men. The children, however, looked at each other as if they would say, "We know better, for we were with them in the gold castle."

Some time after, when the children were again gathering wood in the forest, the brother said, "Do you still remember my having a red mantle round me, my wearing a crown and sitting on a gold throne, and being called King Wichtel the First?"

"Of course I remember," said the sister, "for I sat near you as a princess on a silver throne, and wore a blue dress dotted with silver stars. I shall never forget how beautiful everything was."

Then said the brother, "If we hadn't dropped any tears on the floor, I might have been a king today, and you a princess. But I don't care," he added and laughingly held up his old jacket.

"Neither do I," said the sister, "it is a thousand times better being home with father and mother, than with the Wichtel men in the gold castle."

"Yes," said the brother, "but I am glad that I have been a king just for once!"

The Princess on the Glass Hill

From *Popular Tales from the Norse*, by Peter
Christen Asbjörnsen and Jörgen Engebretsen Moe.
Translated by Sir George Webbe Dasent.   14 minutes

Once upon a time there was a man who had a meadow
which lay on the side of a mountain, and in the meadow
there was a barn in which he stored hay. But there had not
been much hay in the barn for the last two years, for every
St. John's eve the grass was all eaten down to the ground
during the night. This happened once, and it happened
twice, but then the man got tired of losing his crop, and said
to his sons (he had three of them and the youngest was
nicknamed Boots, of course), "One of you must go and
sleep in the barn on St. John's night, for it is foolish to let
the grass be eaten up again, as it has been the last two
years."

The eldest was quite willing to go to the meadow; he
would watch the grass, he said. So when evening came he
went to the barn and lay down to sleep, but when night
was drawing near, there was such a rumbling and such an
earthquake that the walls and roof shook. The lad jumped
up and took to his heels as fast as he could, and never even
looked back, and the barn remained empty that year just as
it had been for the last two.

Next St. John's eve, the man again said that he could
not go on in this way, losing all the grass in the outlying
field year after year, and that one of his sons must go there
and watch it. So the next oldest son was willing to show
what he could do. He went to the barn and lay down to
sleep, as his brother had done; but when night was near

117

there was a great rumbling, and then an earthquake, which was even worse than that on the former St. John's night, and when the youth heard it he was terrified, and ran off.

The year after, it was Boots' turn, but when he made ready to go the others laughed at him and mocked him. Boots, however, did not trouble himself about what they said, but when evening drew near rambled away to the outlying field. He went into the barn and lay down, but in about an hour's time, the rumbling and creaking began, and it was frightful to hear. "Well, if it gets no worse than that, I can manage to stand it," thought Boots. In a little time the creaking began again, and the earth quaked so that all the hay flew about the barn.

"Oh! If it gets no worse than that, I can manage to stand it," thought Boots. Then came a third rumbling, and a third earthquake, so violent that the boy thought the walls and roof had fallen down, but when that was over everything suddenly grew as still as death around him. "I am pretty sure that it will come again," thought Boots, but it did not. Everything was quiet, and everything stayed quiet, and when he had waited a short time he heard something outside the barn door. He stole away to the door, to see what was there and a horse was standing, eating. It was so fine a horse that Boots had never seen one like it before, and a saddle and bridle lay upon it, and a complete suit of armor for a knight. Everything was of copper.

"Ha, ha! It is you who eats up our hay then," thought the boy, "but I will stop that." So he took out his steel for striking fire, and threw it over the horse. It became so tame that the boy could do what he liked with it. So he mounted it and rode away to a place which no one knew of but himself, and there he tied it up. When he went home again, his brothers laughed and asked how he had got on.

"I lay in the barn till the sun rose, but I saw nothing and heard nothing," said the boy. "Heaven knows what there was to make you two so frightened."

"Well, we shall soon see whether you have watched the meadow or not," answered the brothers, but when they got there the grass was all standing just as long and as thick as it had been the night before.

The next St. John's eve it was the same thing once again; neither of the two brothers dared to go to the outlying field to watch the crop, but Boots went, and everything happened exactly as before: first, there was a rumbling and an earthquake, and then there was another, and then a third; but all three earthquakes were very much more violent than they were the year before. Then everything became still as death again, and the boy heard something outside the barn door, so he stole as softly as he could to the door, and again there was a horse. It was far larger and fatter than the first, and it had a saddle on its back, and a bridle, too, and a full suit of armor for a knight. All was of bright silver.

"Ho, ho!" thought the boy, "it is you who eats our hay in the night. But I will put a stop to that." So he took out his steel for striking fire, and threw it over the horse, and the beast stood there as quiet as a lamb. Then the boy rode this horse, too, away to the place where he kept the other, and went home again.

"I suppose you will tell us that you have watched well again this time," said the brothers.

"Well, so I have," said Boots. So they went there again, and the grass was standing as high and as thick as it had been before.

When the third St. John's night came, neither of the two elder brothers dared to lie in the outlying barn to watch the grass, but Boots went and everything happened just the same as on the two former nights. There were three earthquakes, each worse than the other, and the last flung the boy from one wall of the barn to the other, but then everything suddenly became still as death. When he had waited a short time, he heard something outside the barn door; then he once more stole to the door, and behold, a horse was standing outside it.

"Ho, ho! It is you then, who is eating up our hay this time," thought the boy, "but I will put a stop to that." So he pulled out his steel for striking fire, and threw it over the horse, and it stood still and the boy could do just what he liked with it. He mounted it and rode away to the place where he had the two others, and then he went home again. The two brothers mocked him just as they had done before, but Boots told them to go to the field and see for themselves. They did, and this time too the grass was standing, looking as fine and as thick as ever.

Now, the king of the country in which Boots' father dwelt had a daughter whom he would give to the one who could ride up to the top of a high hill of glass, slippery as ice. Upon the very top of this, the king's daughter was to sit with three gold apples in her lap, and the man who could ride up and take the three golden apples should marry her, and have half the kingdom. The princess was very beautiful, and all who saw her fell violently in love with her. So it is needless to say that all the princes and knights were eager to win her, and half the kingdom besides.

When the day appointed by the king had come, there were a host of knights and princes under the glass hill. Boots' two brothers were there, too, but they would not hear of letting him go with them, for he was dirty and black with sleeping and grubbing among the ashes.

"Well, then, I will go all alone by myself," said Boots to himself.

When the two brothers got to the glass hill, all the princes and knights were trying to ride up it, and their horses were in a foam; but it was all in vain, for no sooner did the horses set foot upon the hill than down they slipped. Nor was that strange, for the hill was as smooth as a glass windowpane, and as steep as the side of a house. But they were all eager to win the king's daughter and half the kingdom, so they rode and they slipped, and thus it went on.

The king was just thinking that he would proclaim that the riding should begin afresh on the following day, when suddenly a knight came riding up on a fine horse, wearing armor of copper. He rode for a long way—it may have been a third of the way up the hill—then he turned his horse round and rode down again. But the princess thought that she had never seen so handsome a knight. And when she saw that he was turning his horse back, she threw one of the golden apples down after him, and it rolled into his shoe. When he had come down from the hill he rode away so fast that no one knew what had become of him.

In the evening, all the princes and knights were bidden to present themselves before the king, so that he who had ridden so far up the glass hill might show the golden apple which the king's daughter had thrown down, but no one came who had anything to show.

That night Boots' brothers came home again and had a long story to tell about the riding at the glass hill.

"Oh! I should have liked to see him, too, that I should," said Boots, who was as usual sitting by the chimney among the cinders.

"You, indeed!" said the brothers.

Next day the brothers set out, and this time Boots again begged them to let him go with them, but they said he was not fit to go, for he was much too ugly and dirty. "Well, well, then I will go all by myself," said Boots to himself. So the brothers went to the glass hill, and all the princes and knights began to ride again. They rode and they slipped as they had done the day before, and not one of them could even get so much as a yard up the hill. When they had tired out their horses, they had to stop altogether. But again just as the king was about to proclaim that the riding should take place next day for the last time, came a knight riding on a steed that was much finer than that which

121

the knight in copper armor had ridden. This knight had silver armor and a silver saddle and bridle. The knight rode straight to the glass hill, and went still farther up than the knight in copper armor had gone; but when he had ridden two thirds of the way up, he turned his horse, and rode down again. The princess liked this knight still better than she had liked the other, and when she saw him turning back, she threw the second apple after him, and it rolled into his shoe. As soon as he got down the glass hill, he rode away so fast that no one could see what had become of him.

In the evening, when everyone was to appear before the king and princess, one knight went in after the other, but none of them had the golden apple to show.

The two brothers went home as they had done before and told how things had gone.

"But last of all," they said, "came one in silver armor. He took his horse two thirds of the way up the hill, but then he turned back. He was a fine fellow," said the brothers, "and the princess threw the second golden apple to him!"

"Oh, how I should have liked to see him too!" said Boots.

"You, indeed!" said the brothers.

On the third day everything went just as before. Boots wanted to go with them to look at the riding, but the two brothers would not have him in their company, and when they got to the glass hill, there was no one who could ride even so much as a yard up it. Everyone waited for the knight in silver armor, but he was neither to be seen nor heard. At last, after a long time, came a knight riding upon a horse that was such a fine one, its equal had never yet been seen. The knight had golden armor so bright that it shone and dazzled everyone. He rode straight away to the glass hill, and galloped up it as if it were no hill at all. As soon as he had ridden to the top, he took the third golden apple from the lap of the princess and then turned and rode down again, and vanished from their sight before anyone was able to say a word to him.

When the two brothers came home, they again had much to tell of how the riding had gone off that day, and about the knight in the golden armor.

"He was such a fine fellow!" they said. "So grand a knight isn't to be found in the wide world."

"Oh, how I should have liked to see him too!" said Boots.

Next day all the knights and princes were to appear before the king and princess, in order that he who had a golden apple might produce it. They all went in turn, first princes, and then knights, but none of them had a golden apple.

"But somebody must have one," said the king, "for with our own eyes we all saw a man ride up and take it." So he commanded that everyone in the kingdom should come to the palace, and see if they could show the apple. Well, they all came, one after another, but no one had a golden apple, and after a long, long time, Boots' two brothers came. They were the last of all, so the king asked them if there was any one else in the kingdom who hadn't come.

"Oh, yes, we have a brother," said the two, "but he doesn't have the golden apples! He never left the cinder heap on any of the three days."

"Never mind that," said the king. "As everyone else has come to the palace, let him come too."

So Boots was forced to go to the king's palace.

"Have you a golden apple?" asked the king.

"Yes, here is the first, and here is the second, and here is the third, too," said Boots, and he took all three golden apples out of his pocket, and at the same time threw off his sooty rags and stood before them in his bright golden armor.

123

"Yes!" said the king. "You shall have my daughter, and the half of my kingdom, and you have well earned both!"

So they got ready for the wedding, and Boots married the princess, and there was great merrymaking at the bridal feast, for they could all be merry though they couldn't ride up a hill of glass.

The Steadfast Tin Soldier

Adapted from the story by Hans Christian Andersen.   10 minutes

There were once five and twenty tin soldiers, all brothers, for they were the offspring of the same old tin spoon. Each man shouldered his gun, kept his eyes well to the front, and wore the smartest red and blue uniform imaginable. The first thing they heard in their new world, when the lid was taken off the box, was a little boy clapping his hands and crying, "Soldiers, soldiers." It was his birthday and they had been given to him, so he lost no time in setting them up on the table. All the soldiers were exactly alike with one exception, and he differed from the rest in having only one leg. For he was made last, and there was not quite enough tin left to finish him. However he stood just as well on his one leg as the others on two, in fact he was the very one who was to become famous. On the table where they were being set up, were many other toys; but the chief thing which caught the eye was a delightful paper castle. You could see through the tiny windows, right into the rooms. Outside there were some little trees surrounding a small mirror representing a lake, whose surface reflected the waxen swans which were swimming about on it. It was altogether charming, but the prettiest thing of all was a little maiden standing at the open door of the castle. She, too, was cut out of paper, but she wore a dress of the lightest gauze, with a dainty little blue ribbon over her shoulders, by way of a scarf, set off by a brilliant spangle, as big as her whole face. The little maid was stretching out both arms, for she was a dancer, and in the dance, one of her legs was

125

raised so high into the air that the tin soldier could see absolutely nothing of it, and supposed that she, like himself, had but one leg.

"That would be the very wife for me!" he thought, "but she is much too grand. She lives in a palace, while I only have a box, and then there are five and twenty of us to share it. No, that would be no place for her, but I must try to make her acquaintance!" Then he lay down full length behind a snuffbox, which stood on the table. From that point he could have a good look at the little lady, who continued to stand on one leg without losing her balance.

Late in the evening the other soldiers were put into the box and the people of the house went to bed. Now was the time for the toys to play. They amused themselves with paying visits, fighting battles, and giving balls. The tin soldiers rustled about in their box, for they wanted to join the games, but they could not get the lid off. The nut-crackers turned somersaults, and the pencil scribbled non-sense on the slate. There was such a noise that the canary woke up and joined in, but his remarks were in verse. The only two who did not move were the tin soldier and the little dancer. She stood as stiff as ever on tiptoe, with her arms spread out. He was equally firm on one leg, and he did not take his eyes off her for a moment.

Then the clock struck twelve. Pop! Up flew the lid of the snuffbox, but there was no snuff in it, no! There was a little black goblin, a sort of jack-in-the-box.

"Tin soldier!" said the goblin, "have the goodness to keep your eyes to yourself!"

But the tin soldier pretended not to hear. "Ah, you just wait till tomorrow," said the goblin.

In the morning when the children got up they put the tin soldier on the window frame, and whether it was caused by the goblin or by a puff of wind, I do not know, but all at once the window burst open and the soldier fell head fore-most from the third story.

It was a terrific descent, and he landed at last, with his leg in the air, and rested on his cap, with his bayonet fixed between two paving stones. The maid servant and the little boy ran down at once to look for him. Although they almost trod on him, they could not see him. Had the soldier called out, "Here I am," they could easily have found him, but he did not think it proper to shout when he was in uniform.

Presently it began to rain, and the drops fell faster and faster, till there was a regular torrent. When it was over two street boys came along.

"Look," said one, "there is a tin soldier. He shall go for a sail."

So they made a boat out of a newspaper and put the soldier into the middle of it, and he sailed away down the gutter. Both boys ran alongside clapping their hands. Good heavens! what waves there were in the gutter. What a current, but then it certainly had rained cats and dogs. The paper boat danced up and down, and now and then whirled round and round. A shudder ran through the tin soldier, but he remained undaunted and did not move a muscle. He only looked straight ahead, with his gun shouldered. All at once the boat drifted under a long wooden tunnel, and it became as dark as it was in the box.

"Where on earth am I going now?" he thought. "Well, well, it is all the fault of that goblin. Oh, if only the little maiden were with me in the boat it might be twice as dark for all I should care!"

At this moment a big water rat, who lived in the tunnel, came up.

"Have you a pass?" asked the rat. "Hand up your pass!" The tin soldier did not speak, but clung still tighter to his gun. The boat rushed on, the rat close behind. How he gnashed his teeth and shouted to the bits of stick and straw. "Stop him, stop him, he hasn't paid the toll! He hasn't shown his pass!"

But the current grew stronger and stronger. The tin soldier could see daylight before him at the end of the tunnel, but he also heard a roaring sound, fit to strike terror to the bravest heart. Just imagine! Where the tunnel ended the stream rushed straight into a big canal. That would be just as dangerous for him as it would be for us to shoot a great rapid.

He was so near the end now that it was impossible to stop. The boat dashed on, the poor little tin soldier held himself as stiff as he could; no one should say of him that he even winced.

The boat swirled round three or four times and filled with water to the edge. It must sink. The tin soldier stood up to his neck in water and the boat sank deeper and deeper. The paper became limper and limper and at last the water went over his head. Then he thought of the pretty little dancer, whom he was never to see again, and this refrain rang in his ears.

Onward! onward! soldier!
For death thou canst not shun.

At last the paper gave way entirely and the soldier fell through. At the same moment he was swallowed by a big fish.

Oh! how dark it was inside the fish, it was even worse than being in the tunnel. And then it was so narrow. But the tin soldier was as dauntless as ever, and lay full length shouldering his gun.

The fish rushed about and made the most frantic movements. At last it became quiet, and after a time, a flash like lightning pierced it. The soldier was once more in the broad daylight, and someone called loudly, "A tin soldier!" The fish had been caught, taken to market, sold and brought into the kitchen, where the cook cut it open with a large knife. She took the soldier up by the waist, with two fingers, and carried him into the parlor, where everyone wanted to see the wonderful man who had traveled about in the stomach of a fish. They set him up on the table, and, wonder of wonders, he found himself in the very same room that he had been in before. He saw the very same children, and the toys were still standing on the table, as well as the beautiful castle with the very pretty little dancer.

She still stood on one leg, and held the other up in the air. You see she also was unbending. The soldier was so much moved that he was ready to shed tears of tin, but that would not have been fitting. He looked at her, and she looked at him, but they never said a word. At this moment one of the little boys took up the tin soldier, and without rhyme or reason, threw him into the fire. No doubt the little goblin in the snuffbox was to blame for that. The tin soldier stood there, lighted up by the flame, and in the most horrible heat. But whether it was the heat of the real fire or the warmth of his own feelings he did not know. He had lost all his gay color. It might have been from his perilous journey, or it might have been from grief, who can tell?

He looked at the little maiden, and she looked at him, and he felt that he was melting away, but he still managed to keep himself erect shouldering his gun bravely.

A door was suddenly opened, the draught caught the little dancer and she fluttered like a sylph, straight into the fire, to the little tin soldier, blazed up and was gone. By this time the soldier was reduced to a mere lump, and when the maid took away the ashes the next morning, she found him in the shape of a small tin heart. All that was left of the dancer was her spangle, and that was burnt as black as a coal.

The Sun's Sisters

Adapted from the story by Hjalmar Hjorth Boyesen. *St. Nicholas*. March 1889.   20 minutes

There was once a young prince who had no playmates except a peasant lad named Lars. The king did not like to have his son play with such a common boy; but as there were no princes or kings in the neighborhood, he had no choice but to put up with Lars. One day the prince and Lars were shooting at a mark, and Lars hit the bull's-eye again and again, while the prince's arrows did not even hit the target. Then he grew angry and called Lars a lout and a clodhopper. Lars did not mind, for he knew that princes were petted and spoiled, and could not bear to be crossed.

"Now, prince," he said, "let us shoot up into the air and see who can shoot the highest."

The prince, who had a beautiful gilt bow and polished steel-tipped arrows, had no doubt but that he could shoot much higher than Lars, whose bow was a juniper branch which he had himself cut and cured. So he accepted the offer.

"Let us aim at the sun," he cried gayly.

"All right," shouted Lars, and at the same moment they let fly two arrows.

The boys stood looking up until their eyes ached; and after a moment or two, the prince's arrow fell at his side, and he picked it up. Nearly fifteen minutes elapsed before Lars's arrow returned, and when he picked it up, he was astonished to find a drop of blood on the tip of it, to which clung a dazzlingly beautiful golden feather.

"Why—look at that!" cried the boy, with delight. "Isn't it wonderful?"

"Yes, but it is mine," replied the prince. "It was my arrow."

"It was no such thing," said Lars. "I made the arrow myself and ought to know it. Yours are steel tipped and polished."

"I tell you it is my arrow," cried the prince in great anger, "and if you don't give me the feather, it will go ill with you."

Now, Lars would have been quite willing to part with the feather, if the prince had asked him for it, but he was a high spirited lad, and would not be bullied.

"You know as well as I do that the arrow was mine," he said, "and the feather is mine, too, and I won't give it to anybody."

The prince said nothing, but pale with rage, he hurried back to the castle and told his father, the king, that his arrow had brought down a beautiful golden feather and that Lars had taken it from him.

It was to no purpose that Lars showed the king the drop of blood on the rude whittled arrow; he insisted that the feather was the prince's and that Lars was a thief and a robber. But Lars was not to be frightened even by that. He stuck to his story and refused to give up the feather.

"Well, then," said the king, "we'll say that it is yours. But in that case you must be prepared to prove it. When you bring me the golden hen, from whose tail this feather has been shot, then I'll admit that it is yours. But if you fail, you will be burned alive in a barrel of tar."

Now, this was not a pleasant thing, and Lars, when he heard it wished he had never seen the golden feather. But it would be disgraceful to back down now, so he accepted the terms, stuffed a leg of smoked mutton and a dozen loaves of bread, which the cook at the castle gave him, into a bag and started on his journey. But the question now arose, where should he go? Golden hens were not such everyday affairs that he might expect to find them in any barnyard.

Whenever he saw a farmer burning stumps and rubbish at the roadside, he imagined that it was a barrel of tar in which he was to end his days. For all that, he kept trudging on, and when evening came he found himself on the outskirts of a great forest. Being very tired, he put his bag under his head and soon fell asleep. But he had not been sleeping long when he was waked up by something pulling at the bag. He raised himself on his elbow, rubbed his eyes, and to his astonishment saw a big fox who asked him where he was journeying.

"The fact is, I am in a bad scrape," said Lars. "I have got to find a golden hen that has lost a tail feather." And he told the fox his story.

"Hum," said the fox, "that *is* pretty bad. Let me look at the feather."

The boy took it out from his inside vest pocket, and showed it to the fox.

"Ah," said Reynard, when he had examined it, "you know I have a large acquaintance among hens. In fact, I am very fond of them. I shouldn't wonder if I might help you find the one which has lost this feather."

Lars, who had been quite down in the mouth at the prospect of the barrel of tar, was delighted.

"I wish you would bear me company," said he. "If you'll do me a good turn, I'll do you another."

The fox thought that was a fair bargain; and so they shook hands on it, and off they started together.

"Do you know where we are going?" asked Reynard.

"No," said Lars, "but I suppose you do."

"I do. We are going to the Sun's palace. His sisters Dawn and Afterglow live with him, and Dawn has three golden hens. It was one of those you hit with your arrow."

"But will she be willing to part with any of them?" asked the boy.

"Leave that to me," answered Reynard.

Day after day they walked up one hill and down another until they came to the castle of the Sun. It was very beautiful, shining with silver and gold and precious stones. The boy's eyes ached when he looked at it.

"It is best, I think," said Reynard, "to have me sneak into the poultryyard, where the golden hens are, and then I'll bring out the one that has lost its tail feather."

Lars somehow didn't like that plan. He didn't quite trust Reynard in the matter of hens; he knew the fox had a natural weakness for poultry, but, of course, he was too polite to say so.

"No, Reynard," he began, "I am afraid you might come to harm. And you might make too much racket, you know, setting the whole poultryyard in commotion."

"Well, then, you go yourself," said Reynard, somewhat offended, "but take heed of this warning. Look neither to the right nor to the left, and go straight to the poultryyard, seize the hen that has lost one of the three long tail-feathers, and then hasten out as quick as you can."

Lars agreed and went straight to the poultryyard, where he spied the three golden hens, the splendor of which nearly blinded him, grabbed the one that had lost a tail feather, and started again in hot haste for the gate. But as he passed by the wing of the palace he noticed a window, the shutters of which were ajar. A great curiosity to see what was behind them took possession of him. "It would be a pity to leave this beautiful place without looking about a little," he thought. "I can easily catch that hen again if I let her go now, for she is as tame as a house chicken."

So he let the hen go, opened the shutter, and peeped into the room. And what do you think he saw? It was none other than Dawn, the sister of the Sun. She was lying upon her bed, sleeping sweetly like a child that is taking an after-dinner nap. Goodness and kindness were shining from her features, and Lars was filled with such joy at the mere sight of her that he forgot all about the hen and the barrel of tar, and his playmate the prince, and the fox's warning. He did not know that this was her great charm—every one who looked upon her was instantly filled with gladness. Sorrow, . . . care, . . . malice, and hatred instantly fled from the heart of everyone who came into her presence. No wonder Lars couldn't think of hens, when he had so lovely a creature to look upon. For several minutes he stood at the window. Then stealthily, and without thinking of what he was doing, he climbed over the windowsill and step by step drew nearer.

"Oh, how beautiful! How beautiful!" he whispered. "Oh, I must kiss her before I go, or I shall never have peace so long as I live."

And down he stooped and kissed the Sun's sister. You would have supposed now that she would have wakened. But no! She lay perfectly still. Lars would have been content to spend all his life gazing at her. But a strange uneasiness came over him—his errand, the golden hen, the barrel of tar, and all the rest of it came back to his memory slowly, and, with sudden determination, he covered his eyes with his hands, jumped out the window, and started again in search of the hen. But, somehow, the whole world had now a different look to him. Everything had changed, and the golden hen, too. When he tried to catch her, she ran as fast as she could. Lars plunged ahead, reaching out with both his hands, but she slipped from his grasp, and yelled and screamed at the top of her voice. The Sun's sister, aroused by the commotion, rubbed her beautiful eyes, and started in alarm for the poultryyard.

"What are you doing here?" she asked, when she saw the boy chasing her favorite golden hen.

"Oh, well," said Lars, feeling rather bashful, "I was only amusing myself."

134

"Well," said Dawn gently (for she was as good as she was beautiful), "you can't amuse yourself catching my hens unless—unless—"

"Unless what?" asked Lars.

"Unless," and here the face of Dawn grew very sad, "unless you can rescue my sister Afterglow from the Trolls, who carried her off far behind the western mountains many years ago."

Lars hardly knew what to answer to that; he would have liked to consult his friend Reynard before saying anything. But the Sun's sister looked so beautiful that he had not the heart to say her nay, and so he rashly promised. Then he took his leave, and the moment he was outside the gate and couldn't see the radiant face, his heart seemed ready to break with longing and sadness.

"Well, didn't I tell you you would get into mischief?" said Reynard, when he heard Lars' story. "So now we shall have to rescue this Afterglow, too. Well, that'll be no easy matter, and if you can't behave any better than you have done today, then there's really no use in our attempting it."

Lars had to coax and beg for a full hour. Reynard held out long, but at last took pity on Lars and gave in.

Day after day, and night after night, they traveled toward the far mountains in the west, and at last arrived at the castle of the Trolls.

"Now," said the fox, "I shall go in alone, and when I have induced the girl to follow me, I shall hand her over to you, and then you must rush away with her as fast as you can; and leave me to detain the Trolls by my tricks, until you are so far away that they cannot overtake you."

Lars thought that was a capital plan, and stationed himself outside the gate while the fox slipped in. It was early evening, and it was almost dark, and there was a red blaze of light from all the windows in the castle of the Trolls. Reynard, who had been there many a time before and was an old acquaintance of the Trolls, soon perceived that something unusual was going on. So far as he could see, they were having a ball; and the Trolls were all taking turns at dancing with Afterglow—for she was the only girl in the whole company. When they saw the fox one of them cried out:

"Hallo, old Reynard, you have always been a light-footed fellow. Won't you come in and have a dance?"

"Thanks," said Reynard, "I am never loath to dance."

And he placed his paw upon his breast and made his bow to Afterglow, who was darker than her sister Dawn, and more serious, but scarcely less beautiful. She filled the heart of every one who looked upon her, not with buoyant joy and hope, but meditation and gentle sadness. She was sad herself, too, because she hated the ugly Trolls who held her in captivity, and longed to go back to the beautiful palace of her brother, the Sun. So when Reynard asked her to dance, she scarcely looked at him, but allowed him to put his arm about her waist and swing her about to the measure of the music. And Reynard was a fine dancer. Swiftly he moved about, and every time he passed a candle he managed to blow it out. One—two—three!— before anybody knew it, it was pitch dark in the hall, and before the Trolls had recovered from their astonishment, Reynard had danced out through the door into the hall, and out the gate.

"Lars," he cried to the boy, "here is Afterglow. Now take her and hurry away as fast as you can."

Lars did not have to be told that twice; but taking Afterglow by the hand ran as fast as his feet could carry him.

Reynard instantly slipped in again and pretended to help the Trolls to light the candles. But it took him a long time to strike fire with the flint, because the tinder was damp, and if the Trolls had not been as stupid as they were, they would have seen that the fox was making them trouble instead of helping them. After a long while, however,

136

they succeeded in getting the candles lighted, and then they perceived that Afterglow was gone.

"Where is Afterglow? Where is Afterglow?" they all roared in chorus and some of them wept with anger, while others tore their beards and hair with rage.

"Oh, you sly old fox, it is you who have let her escape," shouted one great, fat, furious Troll, "but you shall suffer for it. Just let me get hold of you, and you shan't have another chance to play tricks again."

Instantly they all made a rush for Reynard. But Reynard, as you know, is no easy customer to catch, and the Trolls were no match for him in running. He took good care to lay his course in the direction opposite to that which Lars and Afterglow had taken; and thus, the farther the Trolls ran, the slighter were their chances of recovering her. After a while, however, Reynard grew tired of this game, and then he remembered that there was a big swamp near by, and thither he hastened. But while he sprang lightly from hillock to hillock, the heavy Trolls in their wrath plunged ahead, and before they knew it, they sank down in the marsh up to their very waists. The night passed and when the dawn flushed the east, the fox called out:

"Look, there comes the Sun's sister."

The Trolls, supposing it was Afterglow, turned with one accord toward the light, and instantly, as the first rays of the dawn struck them, they turned into stone. For the Trolls only go abroad in the night, and cannot endure the light of the Sun. And the huge stones, vaguely retaining their shapes, can yet be seen in the marsh in Lapland, where they perished.

Now, Reynard lost no time in seeking Lars and Afterglow, and toward evening he found their tracks, and before morning came, he had overtaken them. When they arrived at the castle of the Sun they were received with great delight, and Dawn and Afterglow, after their long separation, kissed and embraced each other, and wept with joy. Now Lars was at liberty to take the golden hen and depart for the king's castle; but the trouble with him now was that he didn't want to depart. He could not tear himself away from Dawn's radiant presence, but sat as one bewitched staring into her lovely face. And so it came to pass that they became engaged, and Lars promised to come back and marry her, as soon as he had made his peace with his master the king, and presented him with the golden hen.

The king received Lars pretty well, and was delighted to get the golden hen. But when he heard about Dawn the Sun's sister, whom no one could look upon without being filled with gladness, his brow became clouded, and it was easy to see that he was much displeased. So he told Lars that unless he brought the Sun's sister instantly into the court and gave her as a bride to the young prince, he would have to be burned in the barrel of tar after all.

Then Lars remembered that the Sun had two sisters, and that possibly he might induce Afterglow to marry the prince. When he arrived at the palace of the Sun, Dawn was overjoyed to see him. But when he told his story and mentioned, in passing, the tar barrel, she was not quite so well pleased. However, she went to consult Afterglow who, after her experience with the ugly Trolls, was not at all averse to marrying a handsome young prince. So she rode away on a splendid charger with Lars. And the prince, when he heard she was coming, rode out to meet her, and even the old king himself vowed that he had never seen anyone so beautiful. He grew so gentle, courteous and affectionate as he looked at her, that he forgot all about his threats; and when Afterglow asked him what the great pile of tar barrels was for, he felt quite ashamed of himself, and answered:

"Oh, I was going to burn a wretch there; but as I suppose you don't like the smell of burnt wretch on your wedding day, I'll give orders to have it removed."

The next day the wedding was celebrated with great magnificence; and the feasting, dancing, and rejoicing lasted for an entire week. When it was all over, Lars asked the king's permission to go on a long journey. He had no fear of a refusal, for the king had become so nice and gentle since his daughter-in-law had come into the family, that even his best friends hardly recognized him. So he readily granted Lars' request. With a light heart Lars went eastward, until he came to the palace of the Sun. And there he celebrated his wedding with Dawn, and lived with joy until the end of his days. If he is not dead, he is probably living there yet.

Farm

What Dora Did

Adapted from a true story of a Dakota blizzard
by Mrs. M. P. Handy. *St. Nicholas.* September 1888.
6 minutes

One bright morning in January 1886, Dora Kent, the sixteen-year-old daughter of a farmer living near Devil's Lake, Dakota, was busy in her kitchen, preparing the dinner. She had no mother, and being the eldest girl in the family, the charge of the household fell on her shoulders. Her two sisters, one ten and the other four years old, were with her, helping and hindering; while her father and three brothers, one older and two younger than she, were at work in the barn, some twenty yards away.

The thickly frosted windowpanes did not admit much light, but the great stove kept the room comfortable, so that it was not until the room suddenly grew darker, and there came a rattle of ice against the windows, as though handfuls of sand were flung sharply against them, that she was aware of the change in the weather. A blizzard had come upon them in all its fury.

It was not her first experience. Feeling thankful that father and the boys were safe in the barn, she quietly went on with her preparations. Just as the kitchen clock struck the noon hour, she took down the dinner horn.

All well-built Dakota farmhouses have double doors, and she closed the inner door carefully after her before opening the outer one. Standing in the recess between the two, she blew the horn loudly and long.

143

Sheltered though she was, the snow blew thick against her, and the wind was so strong that her stout young arms could scarcely hold the horn. She went back to the kitchen and waited—fifteen minutes—half an hour. By this time the dinner was as cold as a stone; she set it back on the stove to warm, and going to the door tried to blow the horn again. This time the snow drove into the horn, and choked the sounds so that she, herself, could not hear them. Back to the kitchen for fifteen minutes more of anxious waiting; then she said to her ten-year-old sister,

"Alice, take care of Molly and look after dinner. I am going to the barn to see what keeps father and the boys."

"Don't, Dora—please don't," begged Alice, who knew, from having seen frozen cattle and men, what it meant to be out in a blizzard. "They are only waiting till the blizzard is over. You can't do any good, and will be frozen to death just for nothing!"

But Dora answered,

"I must. I feel it in my bones that something is wrong, and I can't stay here!" So, though Alice and Molly sobbed in concert, she heaped fresh coal on the fire, wrapped herself in her warmest clothing, drew on high fur-lined rubber boots, put a flask of brandy in her pocket, and took the compass from the mantleshelf to show her the way; for not even a shadow of the barn (although it was larger than the house) was visible through the storm. Then, taking the clothesline, she tied one end of the rope tightly around her waist, and, making the other fast to the knob of the outer door, set out upon her perilous journey of twenty yards due north, where she knew the barn must be. Again and again she was beaten down to the ground by the violence of the wind; but she struggled on, keeping the direction of the needle of the compass, and at last reached the side of the barn. Thence she carefully felt her way—fortunately taking the right course—and, finding the door, beat on it with all her might. It was opened by her brothers, and, in the same breath, all asked the same question,

"Where is father?"

"I don't know. I came to see!" and "He started for the house half an hour ago, telling us to stay here until he came back," were simultaneous answers.

"Didn't he take a rope?" asked Dora, eagerly.

"Of course he did. It is tied outside somewhere," said the oldest boy, a year or two her senior.

"Then we must follow it and find him. Alice begged me not to come, but I felt sure something was wrong. Come, Joe, we mustn't lose a minute. Harry and Jack must stay here. Do you hear, boys?"

The younger lads begged hard to come too, but Dora and Joe did not stay to listen. "We mustn't risk their lives, too," she said, huskily. They found the rope covered with snow, and to their surprise stretched taut.

"He must have got to the house, safe," said Joe, joyfully.

But Dora shook her head. "No, it doesn't point south, as it would if he were at home. Besides, I shouted all the time as I came along, and we couldn't have passed each other. He has gone the wrong way."

Meanwhile, clinging to each other, they were following the rope, which slanted lower and lower until, a few feet away, they found it wrapped around the root of a small tree. It was harder to keep hold of it now, but Joe had brought a snow-staff with a sharp hook at one end, and with this it was possible to follow the rope's course. They shouted again and again, at the top of their clear, young voices. There was no answer. Still they toiled on, and it was not long (though it seemed an age) before they stumbled over a snow-covered heap.

It was the body of their father lying where, exhausted by cold and fatigue, he had fallen helplessly to the ground.

Raising his head, Dora poured part of the contents of the flask down his throat. He moaned faintly. He was alive! They lifted him, and dragged him along, vainly trying to make him walk, since exercise was the best means of saving his life. Guided by Dora's rope, which she had wound up after a fashion, thanks to her thick fur gloves, they at last reached the warm kitchen, where a vigorous course of rubbing soon restored their father to perfect consciousness, and brought him out of danger.

He had lost his way, and in his bewilderment had gone around the tree, unconsciously crossing his rope. Thence he had gone to the end of his tether, and in trying to get back to the barn, had found the rope frozen fast to the ground. In his efforts to free it, he had been blown down, and thus dropped the end which he held—for he had not taken Dora's wise precaution of tying it around his body. He was unable to find it with his numb fingers. He shouted vainly for aid, and, afraid to move in any direction, wisely remained where he was. He tried hard to keep in motion, but was overcome by cold, and beaten down by the force of the storm. He must inevitably have been frozen to death but for Dora's heroic search for him.

And the boys in the barn? Oh, Joe went for them as soon as their father was safe, and they all ate dinner together, but some three hours later than usual.

Hallowe'en

Hansel and Gretel

Adapted from the story by the Brothers Grimm.

15 minutes

Once upon a time there dwelt on the outskirts of a large forest a poor woodcutter with his wife and his two children; the boy was called Hansel and the girl Gretel. He had always little enough to live on, and once, when there was a great famine in the land, he couldn't even provide them with daily bread. One night, as he was tossing about in bed, full of cares and worry, he sighed and said to his wife, "What's to become of us? How are we to support my poor children, now that we have nothing more for ourselves?"

"I'll tell you what, husband," answered the woman, "early tomorrow we'll take the children out into the thickest part of the wood; there we shall light a fire for them and give them each a piece of bread; then we'll go on to our work and leave them alone. They won't be able to find their way home, and we shall thus be rid of them."

"No, wife," her husband said, "that I won't do; how could I find it in my heart to leave my children alone in the wood? The wild beasts would soon come and tear them to pieces."

"Oh, you fool," said she, "then we must all four die of hunger." And she left him no peace till he consented. "But I can't help feeling sorry for the poor children," added the husband.

The children, too, had not been able to sleep for hunger, and had heard what their step-mother had said to their father. Gretel wept bitterly, and spoke to Hansel, "Now it's all up with us."

"No, no, Gretel," said Hansel, "don't fret yourself; I'll be able to find a way of escape, no fear."

When the old people had fallen asleep he got up, slipped on his little coat, opened the back door and stole out. The moon was shining clearly, and the white pebbles which lay in front of the house glittered like bits of silver. Hansel bent down and filled his pocket with as many of them as he could cram in.

Then he went back and said to Gretel: "Be comforted, my dear little sister, and go to sleep: God will not desert us;" and he lay down in bed again.

At daybreak, even before the sun was up, the woman came and woke the two children. "Get up, you lie-abeds, we're all going to the forest to fetch wood." She gave them each a bit of bread and said: "Here's something for your lunch, but don't eat it up before, for it's all you'll get." Gretel put the bread under her apron, as Hansel had the stones in his pocket.

Then they all set out together on the way to the forest. After they had walked for a little, Hansel stood still and looked back at the house, and this he did again and again. His father observed him and asked, "Hansel, what are you gazing at there, and why do you always remain behind? Take care, and don't lose your footing."

"Oh! father," said Hansel, "I am looking back at my white kitten, which is sitting on the roof, waving me a farewell."

"What a donkey you are!" the woman exclaimed. "That isn't your kitten, that's the morning sun shining on the chimney." But Hansel had not looked back at his kitten, but each time dropped one of the white pebbles out of his pocket on to the path.

When they had reached the middle of the forest the father said, "Now, children, go and fetch a lot of wood, and I'll light a fire that you mayn't feel cold."

Hansel and Gretel heaped up brushwood till they had made a pile nearly the size of a small hill. The brushwood was set fire to, and when the flames leaped high the woman said, "Now lie down at the fire, children, and rest yourselves. We are going into the forest to cut wood. When we've finished we'll come back and fetch you."

Hansel and Gretel sat down beside the fire, and at midday ate their little bits of bread. They heard the strokes of the axe, so they thought their father was quite near. But it was no axe they heard, but a bough he had tied to a dead tree, that was blown about by the wind. And when they had sat for a long time they fell fast asleep. When they awoke at last it was pitch dark. Gretel began to cry, and said: "How are we ever to get out of the wood?" But Hansel comforted her. "Wait a bit," he said, "till the moon is up, and then we'll find our way." And when the full moon had risen he took his sister by the hand and followed the pebbles, which shone like new threepenny bits, and showed them the path. They walked all through the night, and at daybreak reached their father's house again. They knocked at the door, and when the woman opened it she exclaimed, "You naughty children, what a time you've slept in the wood! We thought you were never going to come back." But the father rejoiced, for his conscience had reproached him for leaving his children behind by themselves.

Not long afterwards there was again great dearth in the land, and again the children heard their step-mother say to their father one night, "Everything is eaten up once more; we have only half a loaf in the house, and when that's gone it's all up with us. The children must be got rid of; we'll lead them deeper into the wood this time, so that they won't be able to find their way out again. There is no other way of saving ourselves."

The man's heart smote him heavily, and he thought, "Surely it would be better to share the last bite with one's children!" But his wife wouldn't listen to his arguments, and did nothing but scold and reproach him. If a man yields once he's done for, and so, because he had given in the first time, he was forced to do so the second.

But the children were awake, and had heard the conversation. When the old people were asleep Hansel got up, and wanted to go out and pick up pebbles again, as he had done the first time; but the woman had barred the door, and Hansel couldn't get out. But he consoled his little sister and said: "Don't cry, Gretel, and sleep peacefully, for God is sure to help us."

At early dawn the woman came and made the children get up. They received their bit of bread, but it was even smaller than the time before. On the way to the wood Hansel crumbled it in his pocket, and every few minutes he stood still and dropped a crumb on the ground.

"Hansel, why are you stopping and looking about?" said the father.

"I'm looking back at my little pigeon which is sitting on the roof waving me a farewell," answered Hansel.

"Fool!" said the wife, "that isn't your pigeon, it's the morning sun glittering on the chimney."

But Hansel gradually threw all his crumbs on the path. The woman led the children still deeper into the forest, farther than they had ever been before. Then a big fire was lit again, and the woman said, "Just sit down there, children, and if you're tired you can sleep a bit; we're going into the forest to cut wood, and in the evening when we're finished we'll come back to fetch you."

At midday Gretel divided her bread with Hansel, for he had strewed his all along their path. Then they fell asleep, but nobody came for the poor children. They didn't awake till it was pitch dark, and Hansel comforted his sister, saying, "Only wait, Gretel, till the moon rises, then we shall see the breadcrumbs I scattered along the path. They will show us the way back to the house." When the moon appeared they got up, but they found no

152

crumbs, for the birds had picked them all up. "Never mind," said Hansel to Gretel, "you'll see we'll still find a way out." They wandered about the whole night, and the next day, from morning till evening, but they could not find a path out of the wood. They were very hungry, too, for they had nothing to eat but a few berries they found growing on the ground. And at last they were so tired that their legs refused to carry them any longer, so they lay down under a tree and fell fast asleep.

On the third morning after they had left their father's house they started out again, but only got deeper and deeper into the wood, and now they felt that if help did not come to them soon they must perish. At midday they saw a beautiful little snow-white bird, sitting on a branch, which sang so sweetly that they stopped still and listened to it. And when its song was finished, it flapped its wings and flew on in front of them. They followed it and came to a little house. When they came quite near they saw that the cottage was made of bread and roofed with cakes, while the window was made of transparent sugar. "I'll eat a bit of the roof, and you, Gretel, can eat some of the window, which you'll find a sweet morsel." Hansel stretched up his hand and broke off a little bit of the roof to see what it was like, and Gretel went to the casement and began to nibble at it. Thereupon a shrill voice called out from the room inside,

> Nibble, nibble, little mouse,
> Who's nibbling my house?

The children answered:

> 'Tis Heaven's own child,
> The tempest wild.

and went on eating. Hansel, who thoroughly appreciated the roof, tore down a big bit of it, while Gretel pushed out a whole round windowpane, and sat down the better to enjoy it. Suddenly the door opened, and a very old woman leaning on a staff hobbled out. Hansel and Gretel were terrified.

But the old woman shook her head and said, "Oh, ho! you dear children, who led you here? Just come in and stay with me, no ill shall befall you."

She took them both by the hand and led them into the house, and laid a most sumptuous dinner before them— milk and sugared pancakes, with apples and nuts. After they had finished, two beautiful little white beds were prepared for them, and when Hansel and Gretel lay down in them they felt as if they were in heaven.

The old woman had appeared to be most friendly, but she was really an old witch who had waylaid the children, and had only built the little bread house in order to lure them in. When anyone came into her power, she killed, cooked, and ate him, and held a regular feast day for the occasion. Now, witches have red eyes, and cannot see far, but, like beasts, they have a keen sense of smell, and know when human beings pass by. When Hansel and Gretel fell into her hands she laughed maliciously and said jeeringly, "I've got them now; they shan't escape me."

Early in the morning, before the children were awake, she rose up, and when she saw them both sleeping so peacefully, with their round rosy cheeks, she muttered to herself, "That'll be a dainty bite." Then she seized Hansel with her bony hand, and carried him into a little stable, and barred the door on him. He might scream as much as he liked, it did him no good.

Then she went to Gretel, shook her till she awoke, and cried, "Get up, you lazy-bones, fetch water and cook something for your brother. When he is fat, I'll eat him up." Gretel began to cry bitterly, but it was of no use; she had to do what the wicked witch bade her.

So the best food was cooked for poor Hansel, but Gretel got nothing but crab shells. Every morning the old woman hobbled out to the stable and cried, "Hansel, put out your finger, that I may feel if you are getting fat." But Hansel always stretched out a bone, and the old witch, whose eyes were dim, couldn't see it, and thinking it was Hansel's finger, wondered why he fattened so slowly. When four weeks passed and Hansel still remained thin, she lost patience and determined to wait no longer. "Hi! Gretel," she called to the girl, "be quick and get some water. Hansel may be fat or thin, I'm going to kill him tomorrow and cook him." Oh! how the poor little sister sobbed as she carried the water, and how the tears rolled down her cheeks!

"Kind heaven help us now!" she cried, "if only the wild beasts in the wood had eaten us, then at least we should have died together."

"Just hold your peace," said the old hag, "nothing will help you."

Early in the morning, Gretel had to go out and hang up the kettle full of water, and light the fire. "First we'll bake," said the old woman. "I've heated the oven already and kneaded the dough." She pushed Gretel out to the oven, from which fiery flames were already issuing. "Creep in," said the witch, "and see if it's properly heated, so that we can shove in the bread." For when she had got Gretel in she meant to close the oven and let the girl bake, that she might eat her up too. But Gretel saw what she meant to do, and said, "I don't know how I'm to do it; how do I get in?" "You silly goose!" said the hag, "the opening is big enough; see, I can get in myself," and she crawled towards it, and poked her head into the oven. Then Gretel gave her a shove that sent her right in, shut the iron door, and drew the bolt. Gracious! how she yelled! It was quite horrible; but Gretel fled, and the wretched old woman was left to perish.

Gretel flew straight to Hansel, opened the little stable-door, and cried: "Hansel, we are free; the old witch is dead." Then Hansel sprang like a bird out of a cage when

155

the door is opened. How they rejoiced and fell on each other's necks, jumped for joy, and kissed one another! And as they had no longer any cause for fear, they went into the old hag's house, and there they found, in every corner of the room, boxes with pearls and precious stones. "These are even better than pebbles," said Hansel, and crammed his pockets full of them; and Gretel said, "I too will bring something home," and she filled her apron full.

"But now," said Hansel, "let's go and get well away from the witch's wood." When they had wandered about for some hours, they came to a big lake. "We can't get over," said Hansel. "I see no bridge of any sort or kind." "There's no ferryboat either," answered Gretel. "But look, there swims a white duck; if I ask her, she'll help us over." And she called out,

> Here are two children, mournful very,
> Seeing neither bridge nor ferry;
> Take us upon your white back,
> And row us over, quack, quack!

The duck swam towards them, and Hansel got on her back and bade his little sister sit beside him. "No," answered Gretel, "we should be too heavy a load for the duck; she shall carry us across separately." The good bird did this, and when they were landed safely on the other side, the wood became more and more familiar to them, and at length they saw their father's house in the distance. Then they set off on the run, and bounding into the room fell on their father's neck. The man had not passed a happy hour since he left them in the wood. The woman had died. Gretel shook out her apron so that the pearls and precious stones rolled about the room, and Hansel threw down one handful after the other out of his pockets. Thus their troubles were ended, and they all lived happily ever afterward.

King Stork

Adapted from *The Wonder Clock* by Howard Pyle.
15 minutes

Once upon a time there was a drummer marching along the high road, for the fighting was done, and he was coming home from the wars. By and by he came to a wide stream of water, and there sat a bent old man. "Are you going to cross the water?" said he.

"Yes," says the drummer, "I am going to do that if my legs hold out to carry me."

"And will you not help a poor body across?" says the old man.

Now, the drummer was as good natured a lad as ever stood on two legs. "If the young never gave a lift to the old," said he to himself, "the wide world would not be worth while living in." So he took off his shoes and stockings, bent his back and took the old man on it, and away he started through the water.

But this was no common old man whom the drummer was carrying, and he was not long in finding that out, for the farther he went in the water the heavier grew his load —so that, when he was halfway across, his legs shook under him. But by and by he reached the shore, and the old man jumped down from his back.

"Phew!" said the drummer, "I am glad to be here at last!"

And now for the wonder of all this—the old man was an old man no longer, but a splendid tall fellow with hair as yellow as gold. "And who would you think I am?" said he.

But of that the drummer knew no more than the mouse in the haystack, so he shook his head, and said nothing.

"I am king of the storks, and here I have sat for many days, for the wicked one-eyed witch who lives on the glass hill cast a spell on me that I should be an old man until somebody should carry me over the water. You are the first to do that, and you shall not lose by it. Here is a little bone whistle; whenever you are in trouble just blow a turn or two on it, and I will be by to help you."

Thereupon King Stork drew a feather cap out of his pocket and clapped it on his head, and away he flew, for he was turned into a great, long, red-legged stork.

But the drummer trudged on his way until he came to a town over the hill. There he found great posters stuck on the walls. Now the princess of that town was as clever as she was pretty and that was saying a great deal, for she was the handsomest in the whole world. The posters proclaimed that any lad who could answer a question the princess would ask, and would ask a question the princess could not answer, and would catch the bird that she would be wanting, should have her for his wife and half of the kingdom to boot. But whoever should fail in any one of the three tasks should have his head chopped off.

The drummer went off to the king's castle as fast as he could step, and there he knocked on the door, as bold as though his own grandmother lived there.

But when the king heard what the drummer had come for, he took out his handkerchief and began to wipe his eyes, for he had a soft heart, and it made him cry to see another coming to have his head chopped off, as so many had done before him. For there they were, all along the wall in front of the princess' window, like so many apples.

But the drummer was not to be scared away by the king's crying, so in he came, and by and by they all sat down to supper—he and the king and the princess. As for the princess, she was so pretty that the drummer's heart melted inside of him. After a while she asked him if he had come to answer a question of hers, and to ask her a question of his, and to catch the bird that she should be wanting.

"Yes," said the drummer, "I have come to do that very thing."

"Very well, then," says the princess, "just come along tomorrow, and I will ask you my question."

Off went the drummer; he put his whistle to his lips and blew a turn or two, and there stood King Stork, and nobody knew where he stepped from.

"And what do you want?" says he.

The drummer told him everything. "Here you have walked into a pretty puddle," said King Stork, for he knew that the princess was a wicked enchantress. "But see, here is a little cap and a long feather—the cap is a dark-cap, and when you put it on your head one can see you no more than so much thin air. At twelve o'clock at night the princess will come out into the castle garden and will fly away through the air. Then throw your leg over the feather, and it will carry you wherever you want to go."

The clock struck twelve, and the princess came out of her house; but in the garden the drummer was waiting for her with the dark-cap on his head, and he saw her as plain as a pikestaff. She fastened a pair of great wings to her shoulders, and away she flew. But the drummer was as quick with his tricks as she was with hers; he flung his leg over the feather which King Stork had given him, and away he flew after her.

By and by they came to a huge castle of shining steel that stood on a mountain of glass. And it was a good thing for the drummer that he had on his cap of darkness, for all around outside of the castle stood fiery dragons and savage lions to keep anybody from going in without leave.

But not a thread of the drummer did they see. In he walked with the princess, and there was a great one-eyed witch with a beard on her chin, and a nose that hooked over her mouth like the beak of a parrot.

"Uff!" said she, "here is a smell of Christian blood in the house."

"Tut, mother!" says the princess, "how you talk! do you not see that there is nobody with me?" By and by they sat down to supper, the princess and the witch, but it was little the princess ate, for as fast as anything was put on her plate the drummer helped himself to it, so that it was all gone before she could get a bite.

"Look, mother!" she said, "I eat nothing, and yet it all goes from my plate; why is that so?" But that the old witch could not tell her, for she could see nothing of the drummer.

"There was a lad came today to answer the question I shall put to him," said the princess. "Now what shall I ask him by way of a question?"

"I have a tooth in the back part of my head," said the witch, "and it has been grumbling a bit; ask him what it is you are thinking about, and let it be that."

Yes; that was a good question, and the princess would give it to the drummer tomorrow. As for the drummer, you can guess how he grinned, for he heard every word they said.

After a while the princess flew home again, for it was nearly the break of day, and she must be back before the sun rose. And the drummer flew close behind her, but she knew nothing of that.

The next morning up he marched to the king's castle and knocked at the door, and they let him in.

There sat the king and the princess, and lots of folks besides. Well, had he come to answer her question? That was what the princess wanted to know.

Yes, that was the very business he had come about.

160

Very well, this was the question, and he might have three guesses at it. What was she thinking of at that minute?

Oh, it could be no hard thing to answer such a question as that; was it a fine silk dress with glass buttons down the front that she was thinking of now?

No, it was not that.

Then was it a good stout lad like himself she was thinking of for a husband?

No, it was not that.

No? Then it was the bad tooth that had been grumbling in the head of the one-eyed witch for a day or two past, perhaps.

Dear, dear! but you should have seen the princess' face when she heard this! Up she got and off she packed without a single word.

The next night the princess flew away to the house of the one-eyed witch again, but there was the drummer close behind her just as he had been before.

"Uff!" said the one-eyed witch, "here is a smell of Christian blood, for sure and certain." But all the same, she saw no more of the drummer than if he had never been born.

"See, mother," said the princess, "that rogue of a drummer answered my question without winking over it."

"So," said the old witch, "we have missed for once, but the second time hits the mark; he will be asking you a question tomorrow, and here is a book that tells everything that has happened in the world, and if he asks you more than that he is a smart one and no mistake."

After a while the princess flew away home, and the drummer with her.

"And, now, what will we ask her that she cannot answer?" said the drummer; so off he went back of the house, and blew a turn or two on his whistle, and there stood King Stork.

"And what will we ask the princess," said he, "when she has a book that tells her everything?"

King Stork was not long in telling him that. "Just ask her so and so, and so and so," said he, "and she would not dare to answer the question."

Well, the next morning there was the drummer at the castle all in good time; and, had he come to ask her a question? that was what the princess wanted to know.

Oh, yes, he had come for that very thing.

Very well, then, just let him begin, for the princess was ready and waiting, and she wet her thumb, and began to turn over the leaves of her Book of Knowledge.

Oh, it was an easy question the drummer was going to ask, and it needed no big book like that to answer it. The other night he dreamed that he was in a castle all built of shining steel, where there lived a witch with one eye. There was a handsome bit of a lass there who was as great a witch as the old woman herself, but for the life of him he could not tell who she was; now perhaps the princess could make a guess at it.

There the drummer had her, for she did not dare to let folks know that she was a wicked witch like the one-eyed one; so all she could do was to sit there and gnaw her lip. As for the Book of Knowledge, it was no use to her.

But if the king was glad when the drummer answered the princess' question, he was twice as glad when she found she could not answer his. So they went on to the next test.

"The bird I want is the one-eyed raven," said the princess. "Now bring her to me if you want to keep your head off the wall yonder."

Yes, the drummer thought he might do that as well as another thing. So off he went back of the house to talk to King Stork of the matter.

"Look," said King Stork, and he drew a net out of his pocket, as fine as a cobweb and as white as milk. "Take this with you when you go with the princess to the one-eyed witch's house tonight, throw it over the witch's head, and see what will happen; only when you catch the one-eyed raven you are to wring her neck as soon as you lay hands on her, for if you don't it will be the worse for you."

Well, that night off flew the princess, and off flew the drummer at her heels, until they came to the witch's house, both of them.

"And did you take his head this time?" said the witch.

No, the princess had not done that, for the drummer had asked such and such a question, and she could not answer it; all the same, she had him tight enough now, for she had set it as a task upon him that he should bring her the one-eyed raven, and it was not likely he would be up to doing that.

"See," said the old witch when the princess was ready to go, "I will go home with you tonight, and see that you get there safe and sound." So she put on her wings, and away they both flew with the drummer behind them.

"Goodnight," said the witch to the princess, and "Goodnight," said the princess to the witch. But the drummer had his wits about him, and before the old witch could get away he flung the net that King Stork had given him over her head.

But you should have been there to see what happened; for it was a great one-eyed raven, as black as the inside of the chimney, that he had in his net.

Dear, dear, how it flapped its wings and struck with its great beak! But that did no good, for the drummer just wrung its neck, and there was an end of it.

The next morning he wrapped it up in his kerchief, and off he started for the king's castle, and there was the princess waiting for him, for she felt sure the drummer was caught in the trap this time.

"And have you brought the one-eyed raven with you?" she said.

"Oh, yes," said the drummer, and here it was wrapped up in his handkerchief.

But when the princess saw the raven with its neck wrung, she gave a great shriek and fell to the floor. There she lay and they had to pick her up and carry her out of the room.

But everybody saw that the drummer had brought the bird she had asked for, and all were as glad as could be. Then he went off back of the house and blew a turn or two on his whistle, and there stood King Stork. "Here is your dark-cap and your feather," says he, "and it is I who am thankful to you, for they have won me a real princess for a wife."

"Yes, good," says King Stork, "you have won her, sure enough, but the next thing is to keep her; for a lass is not cured of being a witch as quickly as you seem to think. See now, the princess is just as wicked as ever she was before, and if you do not keep your eyes open she will trip you up after all. So listen to what I tell you. Just after you are married, get a bowl of fresh milk and a good, stiff switch. Pour the milk over the princess when you are alone together, and after that hold tight to her and lay on the switch, no matter what happens, for that is the only way to save yourself and to save her."

Well, the drummer promised to do as King Stork told him, and by and by came the wedding day. As soon as he and the princess were alone together he emptied the milk all over her; and caught hold of her and began laying on the switch for dear life.

It was well for him that he had been a soldier and was a brave fellow, for, instead of the princess, he held a great black cat that glared at him with her fiery eyes, and growled and spat like everything. Then, instead of a black cat it was like a savage wolf, that snarled and snapped at the drummer, then it changed to a great snake that lashed its tail and shot its forked tongue and spat fire. But the drummer was no more frightened than he had been before.

Last of all, there stood the princess herself. "Oh, dear husband!" she said, "let me go, and I will promise to be a good wife all the days of my life."

"Very well," said the drummer, "and that is the tune I like to hear."

And that was the way he gained the best of her, whether it was the bowl of milk or the hazel switch is a question you will have to answer for yourselves. All the same the princess tried no more of her tricks on him, I can tell you.

Tamlane

Adapted from *Fairies and Enchanters* by Amabel
Williams-Ellis. Copyright 1934 by Thomas Nelson &
Sons. Reproduced by permission.   12 minutes

Fair Janet sat in her bower, and as she sewed her
silken seam she wished she were out in Carterhaugh forest.
But all the maidens had been forbidden to go, because that
was where the gallants of the court of Elfland disported
themselves, and the older people shook their heads and
said that surely some harm would come to any maid who
went there. But the more Lady Janet sat, and the more
she sewed her seam, the more she wished she were out of
the castle and away in the greenwood. At last she could
bear it no longer; she let seam and needle fall, and without
a word to any one, she kilted her green kirtle above her
knee, and braided up her yellow hair, and she made off to
the greenwood as fast as she could go.

She had not been long among the leaves of the forest
before she saw a fine horse, as white as milk, with gold
trappings, that stood tethered to a tree; and she had scarcely
pulled one double rose, of all that grew there, before, sure
enough, up started a knight, young Tamlane.

"Why do you pluck the rose, Janet? How dare you
break the flowers? How dare you come to Carterhaugh
forest without my leave?"

"I shall pluck the roses just as I please," she said, and
tossed her head. "I shall never ask leave of thee!"

And when she answered him so bold, the young knight
laughed and spoke her fair, and shook the nine silver bells
that hung at his girdle. So all the day Janet and young

Tamlane spent dancing in the glades of the forest, and it seemed as if music blew about them, and they danced as if they could never grow tired.

But at last Lady Janet looked up and saw that the sun was low in the sky, and she knew that she must hurry home to her father's castle if she was to be there before she was missed.

So once again she kilted up her kirtle, and snooded up her hair, and went back home as fast as she was able. But this time her feet went heavily.

And when she came to her father's castle, and walked across the great hall, she looked so pale and wan that the four and twenty ladies that were playing at ball there wondered to see her.

"Did you get a fright in the forest, Lady Janet," said they, "that you look so wan and pale? Or do you ail with some sickness?"

The next day it was no better. The four and twenty ladies were playing at chess, and Lady Janet, she that used to be the flower among them all, sat drooping and sad, and she could think of nothing but young Tamlane and of dancing in the forest.

Then there spoke an old gray knight that stood at guard on the castle wall, "Alas, fair Janet!" he said, "I doubt it's with the fairies you have been. If your father gets to hear of this we shall all be blamed, for no good ever came of going with the fairies."

"Hold your tongue," said she, and wept. "Oh, if my love were an earthly knight, why he'd be the fairest bridegroom that any maid might wed.

> "The steed that my true love rides on
> Is fleeter than the wind;
> With silver he is shod before
> With burning gold behind."

But in her heart she feared that he was one of the elf knights. And still she pined, and still all her thought was of Carterhaugh and of young Tamlane. At last she could bear it no longer, let the danger be what it might. So once more she kilted up her green kirtle above her knee and snooded up her yellow hair, and slipped away again to Carterhaugh. But this time she could see neither horse nor knight.

So once more she began to pluck herbs and leaves, when, just as before, up started young Tamlane. Then she says to him: "Tell me, tell me, Tamlane," she said, "were you ever in a holy chapel? Are you a christened soul? Or, as I fear, are you one of the Elf knights?"

And then he told her that though indeed he lived at the Elf Queen's court he was of human parentage, the son of a knight and a lady; and they sat down together and he told her his history:

> "Roxburgh he was my grandfather,
>   Took me with him to bide;
> And once it fell upon a day
>   As hunting I did ride,
> There came a wind out of the north,
>   A cold wind and a snell,
> A dead sleep it came over me
>   And from my horse I fell;
> And the Queen o' Fairies she took me
>   In yon green hill to dwell."

He told her that it was a fair country and a pleasant life, and that he had great honor in the fairy court and with the queen.

"A man might dwell there forever, Janet, but for one thing."

And then he told her how he had been with the fairies nearly seven years, and how he knew that at the end of every seven years they must pay a ransom and a tithe to

168

the foul fiends of Hell, and how he feared that this time it was with him they meant to pay, unless some mortal would borrow him—that is, break the spell and win him back again.

Then he told Lady Janet how she might win him back out of fairyland, only there was no time to lose. On the night of Hallowe'en, which was the very next night, the fairy folk ride abroad, and any that would win back her true love from among the fairy company must keep vigil at Miles Cross.

Then said Lady Janet, "But how should I know you, Tamlane, so that I might win you back? How shall I know you among all that company, for you will be riding among a pack of uncouth knights the like I never saw?"

Then he told her what she must do. "You must go down to Miles Cross in the deep of the night, between midnight and one o'clock, and you must fill your hands with holy water, and make a circle round you, and then you must wait and see what you will see. And this is how you can know me among all the others. The fairies will all ride past in companies; to the first company that passes you must say nothing, let them go; to the second company that passes by say nothing, and let them go likewise; but in the third company I shall be riding.

> "O first let pass the black, lady,
>   And then let pass the brown;
> But quickly run to the milk-white steed,
>   And pull his rider down.
>
> "For some ride on the black, lady,
>   And some ride on the brown;
> But I ride on the milk-white steed,
>   A gold star on my crown:
> Because I was an earthly knight
>   They give me that renown

169

"My right hand will be gloved, lady,
    My left hand will be bare,
And that's the token I give thee,
    No doubt I will be there."

Then he told her what would happen next.

"When you know me you must take my horse by the head, and snatch the reins out of my hand, and let fall the bridle, I shall slip down from the horse, and the Queen of Elfland will cry out, 'True Tamlane's stolen away!' Then you must hold me in your arms, and first they will turn me to a newt, and then to a snake, but if ever you will have me for your true love you must hold fast and never let me go. And then, in your arms, lady, they will turn me to a wild deer; but however the deer struggles you must hold it fast. And then in your arms they will turn me to a red-hot iron, but if you love me, as you say, to that, too, you must hold fast and not let go, however it burn you.

"They'll shape me last in your arms, Janet,
    A mother-naked man;
Cast your green mantle over me
    And so shall I be won."

And no sooner had he said that than Tamlane vanished away, and Lady Janet was alone in the forest.

Now, as he had said, the next day was Hallowe'en, so for the third time Janet kilted up her green kirtle above her knee and snooded her yellow hair, and before it was dark midnight she was at Miles Cross, and she cast a circle of holy water round her as he had bidden, and waited for what might befall.

About the dead hour of the night,
    She heard the bridles ring;
And Janet was as glad of that
    As any earthly thing.

All fell out exactly as Tamlane had told her. First went by a company of knights on black horses, and then a company of knights on brown, but when, at the head of the third company she saw the milk-white horse, she rushed forward, seized the bridle, and pulled down the rider. And then there arose an unearthly cry:

"True Tamlane's stolen away! True Tamlane's stolen away!"

And once more all was exactly as Tamlane had told her. Instead of a knight in her arms there was a great newt, but still she gripped and still she held. And then it became a wriggling hissing snake, and still she gripped and still she held. And then in her arms she had a wild struggling deer, but, struggle as he would, she gripped and she held. And then she found that in her two hands was a red-hot iron; but burn as it would, still she gripped and still she held, knowing that only so could she have her heart's desire.

> They shaped him in her arms at last,
>   A mother-naked man;
> She cast her mantle over him,
>   And so her love she won.

> Up then spake the Queen of Fairies
>   Out of a bush of broom,
> "She that has borrow'd young Tamlane
>   Has gotten a stately groom."

> Out then spake the Queen of Fairies,
>   And an angry woman was she,
> "She's taken away the bonniest knight
>   In all my companie!"

"Farewell to you, Tamlane, farewell!" the Queen cried again. "But know you this, that if I had known yesterday what I know tonight, I would have taken out your heart of flesh and put in a heart of stone instead. And if I had known yesterday what I know tonight, I would have taken out your two gray eyes and put in eyes of wood. And if I had known yesterday what I know today, I would have paid a ransom seven times to Hell so could I have kept you!"

And when she had said so, she and all her knights vanished, and Lady Janet and Tamlane went back to her father's castle, and there they were married amid great rejoicing.

Teeny-Tiny

From *Fairy Tales* by Joseph Jacobs.   2 minutes

Once upon a time there was a teeny-tiny woman who
lived in a teeny-tiny house in a teeny-tiny village. Now,
one day this teeny-tiny woman put on her teeny-tiny bonnet,
and went out of her teeny-tiny house to take a teeny-tiny
walk. And when this teeny-tiny woman had gone a teeny-
tiny way, she came to a teeny-tiny gate; so the teeny-tiny
woman opened the teeny-tiny gate, and went into a teeny-
tiny churchyard. And when this teeny-tiny woman had
got into the teeny-tiny churchyard, she saw a teeny-tiny
bone on a teeny-tiny grave, and the teeny-tiny woman said
to her teeny-tiny self, "This teeny-tiny bone will make
me some teeny-tiny supper." So the teeny-tiny woman put
the teeny-tiny bone into her teeny-tiny pocket, and went
home to her teeny-tiny house.

Now when the teeny-tiny woman got home to her
teeny-tiny house, she was a teeny-tiny bit tired; so she
went up her teeny-tiny stairs to her teeny-tiny bed, and
put the teeny-tiny bone into a teeny-tiny cupboard. And
when this teeny-tiny woman had been asleep a teeny-
tiny time, she was awakened by a teeny-tiny voice from
the teeny-tiny cupboard, which said:

"Give me my bone!"

And this teeny-tiny woman was a teeny-tiny frightened,
so she hid her teeny-tiny head under the teeny-tiny clothes
and went to sleep again. And when she had been asleep

173

a teeny-tiny time, the teeny-tiny voice again cried out from the teeny-tiny cupboard a teeny-tiny louder,

"Give me my bone!"

This made the teeny-tiny woman a teeny-tiny more frightened, so she hid her teeny-tiny head a teeny-tiny further under the teeny-tiny clothes. And when the teeny-tiny woman had been asleep again a teeny-tiny time, the teeny-tiny voice from the teeny-tiny cupboard said again a teeny-tiny louder,

"GIVE ME MY BONE!"

And this teeny-tiny woman was a teeny-tiny bit more frightened, but she put her teeny-tiny head out of the teeny-tiny clothes, and said in her loudest teeny-tiny voice,

"TAKE IT!"

Humor

Clever Else

From the story by the Brothers Grimm.   6 minutes

There was once a man who had a daughter who was called "Clever Else," and when she was grown up, her father said she must be married, and her mother said,

"Yes, if we could only find some one that she would consent to have."

At last one came from a distance, and his name was Hans, and when he proposed to her, he made it a condition that Clever Else should be very careful as well.

"Oh," said the father, "she does not want for brains."

"No, indeed," said the mother, "she can see the wind coming up the street and hear the flies cough."

"Well," said Hans, "if she does not turn out to be careful too, I will not have her."

Now when they were all seated at table, and had well eaten, the mother said, "Else, go into the cellar and draw some beer."

Then Clever Else took down the jug from the hook on the wall, and as she was on her way to the cellar she rattled the lid up and down so as to pass away the time. When she got there, she took a stool and stood it in front of the cask, so that she need not stoop and make her back ache with needless trouble. Then she put the jug under the tap and turned it, and while the beer was running, in order that her eyes should not be idle, she glanced hither and thither, and finally caught sight of a pickaxe that the workmen had left sticking in the ceiling just above her head. Then Clever Else began to cry, for she thought,

177

"If I marry Hans, and we have a child, and he grows big, and we send him into the cellar to draw beer, that pickaxe might fall on his head and kill him."

So there she sat and cried with all her might, lamenting the misfortune to come. All the while they were waiting upstairs for something to drink, and they waited in vain. At last the mistress said to the maid, "Go down to the cellar and see why Else does not come."

So the maid went, and found her sitting in front of the cask crying with all her might.

"What are you crying for?" said the maid.

"Oh, dear me," answered she, "how can I help crying? If I marry Hans, and we have a child, and he grows big, and we send him here to draw beer, perhaps the pickaxe may fall on his head and kill him."

"Our Else is clever indeed!" said the maid, and directly sat down to bewail the misfortune to come. After a while, when the people upstairs found that the maid did not return, and they were becoming more and more thirsty, the master said to the boy, "You go down into the cellar, and see what Else and the maid are doing."

The boy did so, and there he found both Clever Else and the maid sitting crying together. Then he asked what was the matter.

"Oh, dear me," said Else, "how can we help crying? If I marry Hans, and we have a child, and he grows big, and we send him here to draw beer, the pickaxe might fall on his head and kill him."

"Our Else is clever indeed!" said the boy, and sitting down beside her, he began howling with a good will. Upstairs they were all waiting for him to come back, but as he did not come, the master said to the mistress, "You go down to the cellar and see what Else is doing."

So the mistress went down and found all three in great lamentations and when she asked the cause, then Else told her how the future possible child might be killed as soon

178

as he was big enough to be sent to draw beer, by the pickaxe falling on him. Then the mother at once exclaimed, "Our Else is clever indeed!" and sitting down, she wept with the rest.

Upstairs the husband waited a little while, but as his wife did not return, and as his thirst constantly increased, he said, "I must go down to the cellar myself, and see what has become of Else."

And when he came into the cellar, and found them all sitting and weeping together, he was told that it was all owing to the child that Else might possibly have, and the possibility of his being killed by the pickaxe so happening to fall just at the time the child might be sitting underneath it drawing beer. When he heard all this, he cried, "How clever is our Else!" and sitting down, he joined his tears to theirs.

The intended bridegroom stayed upstairs by himself a long time, but as nobody came back to him, he thought he would go himself and see what they were all about. And there he found all five lamenting and crying most pitifully, each one louder than the other.

"What misfortune has happened?" cried he.

"Oh, my dear Hans," said Else, "if we marry and have a child, and he grows big, and we send him down here to draw beer, perhaps the pickaxe which has been left sticking up there might fall down on the child's head and kill him; and how can we help crying at that!"

"Now," said Hans, "I cannot think that greater sense than that could be wanted in my household; so as you are so clever, Else, I will have you for my wife," and taking her by the hand he led her upstairs, and they had the wedding at once.

A little while after they were married, Hans said to his wife, "I am going out to work, in order to get money; you go into the field and cut the corn, so that we may have bread."

"Very well, I will do so, dear Hans," said she. And after Hans was gone, she cooked herself some nice stew, and took it with her into the field.

And when she got there, she said to herself, "Now, what shall I do? Shall I reap first, or eat first? All right, I will eat first."

Then she ate her fill of stew, and when she could eat no more, she said to herself, "Now, what shall I do? Shall I reap first, or sleep first? All right, I will sleep first." Then she lay down in the corn and went to sleep.

And Hans got home, and waited there a long while, and Else did not come, so he said to himself, "My clever Else is so industrious that she never thinks of coming home and eating."

But when evening drew near and still she did not come, Hans set out to see how much corn she had cut; but she had cut no corn at all, but there she was lying in it asleep. Then Hans made haste home, and fetched a bird-net with little bells and threw it over her; and still she went on sleeping. And he ran home again and locked himself in, and sat himself down on his bench to work. At last, when it was beginning to grow dark, Clever Else woke, and when she got up and shook herself, the bells jingled at each movement that she made. Then she grew frightened, and began to doubt whether she were really Clever Else or not, and said to herself, "Am I, or am I not?"

And not knowing what answer to make, she stood for a long while considering; at last she thought, "I will go home to Hans and ask him if I am I, or not; he is sure to know."

So she ran to the door of her house, but it was locked; then she knocked at the window and cried, "Hans, is Else within?"

"Yes," answered Hans, "she is in."

Then she was in a greater fright than ever, and crying, "Oh dear, then I am not I."

She went to inquire at another door, but the people hearing the jingling of the bells would not open to her, and she could get in nowhere. So she ran away beyond the village and since then no one has seen her.

How the Good Gifts Were Used by Two

From *The Wonder Clock* by Howard Pyle.

15 minutes

This is the way that this story begins:

Once upon a time there were a rich brother and a poor brother, and the one lived across the street from the other.

The rich brother had all of the world's gear that was good for him and more besides; as for the poor brother, why, he had hardly enough to keep soul and body together, yet he was contented with his lot, and contentment did not sit back of the stove in the rich brother's house; wherefore in this the rich brother had less than the poor brother.

Now these things happened in the good old times when the saints used to be going hither and thither in the world upon this business and upon that. So one day, who should come traveling to the town where the rich brother and the poor brother lived, but Saint Nicholas himself.

Just beside the town gate stood the great house of the rich brother; thither went the saint and knocked at the door, and it was the rich brother himself who came and opened it to him.

Now, Saint Nicholas had had a long walk of it that day, so that he was quite covered with dust, and looked no better than a common beggar; and when the rich brother heard him ask for a night's lodging at his fine, great house, he gaped like a toad in a rain storm. What! Did the traveler think that he kept a free lodging house for beggars? If he did he was bringing his grist to the wrong mill; there was no place for the likes of him in

182

the house, and that was the truth. But yonder was a poor man's house across the street, if he went over there perhaps he could get a night's lodging and a crust of bread. That was what the rich brother said, and after he had said it he banged the door, and left Saint Nicholas standing on the outside.

So, now there was nothing for good Saint Nicholas to do but to go across the street to the poor brother's house, as the other had told him to do. Rap! tap! tap! he knocked at the door, and it was the poor brother who came and opened it for him.

"Come in, come in!" says he, "come in and welcome!"

So in came Saint Nicholas, and sat himself down behind the stove where it was good and warm, while the poor man's wife spread before him all that they had in the house—a loaf of brown bread and a crock of cold water from the town fountain.

"And is that all that you have to eat?" said Saint Nicholas.

Yes; that was all that they had.

"Then, maybe, I can help you to better," said Saint Nicholas. "So bring me hither a bowl and a crock."

You may guess that the poor man's wife was not long in fetching what he wanted. When they were brought, the saint blessed the one and passed his hand over the other.

Then he said, "Bowl be filled!" and straightway the bowl began to boil up with a good rich meat pottage until it was full to the brim. Then the saint said, "Bowl be stilled!" and it stopped making the broth, and there stood as good a feast as man could wish for.

Then Saint Nicholas said, "Crock be filled!" and the crock began to bubble up with the best of beer. Then he said, "Crock be stilled!" and there stood as good drink as man ever poured down his throat.

Down they all sat, the saint and the poor man and the poor man's wife, and ate and drank till they could eat and drink no more, and whenever the bowl and the crock grew empty, the one and the other became filled at the bidding.

The next morning the saint trudged off the way he was going, but he left behind him the bowl and the crock, so that there was no danger of hunger and thirst coming to that house.

Well, the world jogged along for a while, maybe a month or two, and life was as easy for the poor man and his wife as an old shoe. One day the rich brother said to *his* wife. "See now, luck seems to be stroking our brother over yonder the right way; I'll just go and see what it all means."

So over the street he went, and found the poor man at home. Down he sat back of the stove and began to chatter and talk and talk and chatter, and the upshot of the matter was that, bit by bit, he dragged out the whole story from the poor man. Then nothing would do but he must see the bowl and the crock at work. So the bowl and the crock were brought and set to work and—Hui!—how the rich brother opened his eyes when he saw them making good broth and beer of themselves.

And now he must and would have that bowl and crock. At first the poor brother said "No," but the other bargained and bargained until, at last, the poor man consented to let him have the two for a hundred dollars. So the rich brother paid down his hundred dollars, and off he marched with what he wanted.

When the next day had come, the rich brother said to his wife, "Never you mind about the dinner today. Go you into the harvest field, and I will see to the dinner." So off went the wife with the harvesters, and the husband stayed at home and smoked his pipe all the morning, for he knew that dinner would be ready at the bidding. So when noontide had come he took out the bowl and the crock, and, placing them on the table, said, "Bowl be filled! Crock be filled!" and straightway they began making broth and beer as fast as they could.

In a little while the bowl and the crock were filled, and then they could hold no more, so that the broth and beer ran down all over the table and the floor. Then the rich brother was in a pretty pickle, for he did not know how to bid the bowl and the crock to stop from making what they were making. Out he ran and across the street to the poor man's house, and meanwhile the broth and beer filled the whole room until it could hold no more, and then ran out into the gutters so that all the pigs and dogs in the town had a feast that day.

"Oh, dear brother!" cried the rich man to the poor man, "do tell me what to do or the whole town will soon be smothered in broth and beer."

But, no; the poor brother was not to be stirred in such haste; they would have to strike a bit of a bargain first. So the upshot of the matter was that the rich brother had to pay the poor brother another hundred dollars to take the crock and bowl back again.

See, now, what comes of being covetous!

As for the poor man, he was well off in the world, for he had all that he could eat and drink, and a stockingful of money back of the stove besides.

Well, time went along as time does, and now it was Saint Christopher who was thinking about taking a little journey. "See, brother," said Saint Nicholas to him, "if you chance to be jogging by yonder town, stop at the poor man's house, for there you will have a warm welcome and plenty to eat."

But when Saint Christopher came to the town, the rich man's house seemed so much larger and finer than the poor man's house, that he thought that he would ask for lodging there.

185

But it fared the same with him that it had with Saint Nicholas. Prut! Did he think that the rich man kept free lodgings for beggars? And—bang!—the door was slammed in his face, and off packed the saint with a flea in his ear.

Over he went to the poor man's house, and there was a warm welcome for him, and good broth and beer from the bowl and the crock that Saint Nicholas had blessed. After he had supped he went to bed, where he slept as snug and warm as a mouse in the nest.

Then the good wife said to the husband, "See, now, the poor fellow's shirt is none too good for him to be wearing. I'll just make him another while he is sleeping, so that he'll have a decent bit of linen to wear in the morning."

So she brought her best roll of linen out of the closet, and set to work stitching and sewing, and never stopped till she had made the new shirt to the last button. The next morning, when the saint awoke, there lay the nice, new, clean shirt, and he put it on and gave thanks for it.

Before he left the house the poor man took him aside, and emptied the stockingful of silver money on the table, and bade the saint take what he wanted, "For," says he, "a penny or two is never amiss in the great world."

After that it was time for the traveler to be jogging; but before he went he said, "See, now, because you have been so kind and so good to a poor wayfarer, I will give you a blessing; whatever you begin doing this morning, you shall continue doing till sunset." So saying, he took up his staff and went his way.

After Saint Christopher had gone the poor man and his wife began talking together as to what would be best for them to be doing all of the day, and one said one thing and the other said the other, but every plug was too small for the hole, as we say in our town, for nothing seemed to fit the case.

"Come, come," said the good woman, "here we are losing time that can never be handled again. While we are talking the matter over I will be folding the linen that is left from making the shirt."

"And I," said the good man, "will be putting the money away that the holy man left behind him."

So the wife began folding the linen into a bundle again, and the man began putting away the money that he had offered in charity. Thus they began doing, and thus they kept on doing; so that by the time the evening had come the whole house was full of fine linen, and every tub and bucket and mug and jug about the place was brimming with silver money. As for the good couple, their fortune was made, and that is the heart of the whole matter in four words.

That night who should come from across the street but the rich brother, with his pipe in his mouth and his hands in his pockets. But when he saw how very rich the poor man had become all of a sudden, and what a store of fine linen and silver money he had, he was so wonder struck that he did not know whither to look and what to think.

Dear heart's sake alive! Where did all these fine things come from? That was what he should like to know.

Oh! there was nothing to hide in the matter, and the poor man told all about what had happened.

As for the rich brother, when he found how he had shut his door in the face of good fortune, he rapped his head with his knuckles because he was so angry at his own foolishness. However, crying never mended a torn jacket, so he made the poor brother promise that if either of the saints came that way again, they should be sent over to his house for a night's lodging, for it was only fair and just that he should have a share of the same cake his brother had eaten.

So the poor brother promised to do what the other wanted, and the rich brother went back home again.

Well, a year and a day passed, and then, sure enough, who should come along that way but both the saints together, arm in arm. Rap! tap! tap! they knocked at the poor man's door, for they thought that where they had had good lodging before they could get it again. And so they could and welcome, only the poor brother told them that his rich brother across the street had asked that they should come and lodge at the fine house when they came that way again.

The saints were willing enough to go to the rich brother's house, though they would rather have stayed with the other. So over they went, and when the rich brother saw them coming he ran out to meet them, and shook each of them by the hand, and bade them to come in and sit down back of the stove where it was warm.

But you should have seen the feast that was set for the two saints at the rich brother's house! After supper they were shown to a grand room, where each saint had a bed all to himself, and before they were fairly asleep the rich man's wife came and took away their old shirts, and laid a shirt of fine cambric linen in the place of each. When the next morning came and the saints were about to take their leave, the rich brother brought out a great bag of golden money, and bade them stuff what they would of it into their pockets.

Well, all this was as it should be, and before the two went on their way they said that they would give the same blessing to him and his wife that they had given to the other couple—that whatsoever they should begin doing that morning, that they should continue doing until sunset.

After that they put on their hats and took up their staffs, and off they plodded.

Now the rich brother was a very envious man, and was not contented to do only as well as his brother had done, no indeed! He would do something that would make him even richer than counting out money for himself all day. So down he sat back of the stove and began turning the matter over in his mind, and rubbing up his wits to make them the brighter.

In the meantime the wife said to herself, "See, now, I shall be folding fine cambric linen all day, and the pigs will have to go with nothing to eat. I have no time to waste in feeding them, but I'll just run out and fill their troughs with water at any rate."

So out she went with a bucketful of water which she began pouring into the troughs for the pigs. That was the first thing she did, and after that there was no leaving off, but pour water she must until sunset.

All this while the man sat back of the stove, warming his wits and saying to himself, "Shall I do this? shall I do that?" and answering "No" to himself every time. At last he began wondering what his wife was doing, so out he went to find her. Find her he did, for there she was pouring out water to the pigs. Then if anybody was angry it was the rich man. "What!" cried he, "and is this the way that you waste the gifts of the blessed saints?"

So saying, he looked around, and there lay a bit of a switch on the ground near by. He picked it up, and struck the woman across the shoulders with it, and that was the first thing that he began doing. After that he had to keep on doing the same.

So the woman poured water, and the man stood by and beat her with a little switch until there was nothing left of it, and that was what they did all day.

And what is more, they made such a hubbub that the neighbors came to see what was going forward. They looked and laughed and went away again, and others came, and there stood the two—the woman pouring water and the man beating her with the bit of a switch.

When the evening came, and they left off their work, they were so weary that they could hardly stand; and nothing was to show for it but a broken switch and a wet sty, for even the blessed saints cannot give wisdom to those who will have none of it, and that is the truth.

And such is the end of this story, with only this to tell: There are folks, even in these wise times, who, if they did all day what they began in the morning, would find themselves at sunset doing no better work than pouring pure water to pigs.

That is the small kernel to this great nut.

The Queen Who Couldn't Bake Gingerbread and the King Who Couldn't Play the Trombone

Adapted from the story by Richard Leander, translated by Anna Eichberg. *St. Nicholas.* March 1883.

10 minutes

The King of Mararoni, who was just in the prime of life, got up one morning and sat on the edge of his bed.

The Lord Chamberlain stood before him, and handed him his stockings, one of which had a great hole in the heel.

The stocking was artfully turned so that the hole should not be visible to His Majesty's eyes, and though the king didn't generally mind a ragged stocking as long as he had pretty boots, this time, however, the hole attracted his attention. Horrified, he tore the stocking out of the Lord Chamberlain's grasp, and poking his forefinger through the hole as far down as the knuckle, he remarked, with a sigh, "What is the use of being a king, if I have no queen? What would you say if I should marry?"

"The idea is sublime, Your Majesty," the Lord Chamberlain said, humbly. "I may say that the idea would have suggested itself to me, had I not been certain that Your Royal Highness would, in the course of the day, have mentioned it yourself."

"That will do," said the king, for he was afraid of the Lord Chamberlain's speeches, "but do you think I shall easily find a suitable wife?"

"Good gracious, yes! ten to one," was the reply.

"Don't forget that I am not easily satisfied. If I am to like the princess, she must be very wise and beautiful.

Then there is another and very important condition. You know how fond I am of gingerbread! There isn't a person in my kingdom who understands how to bake it—at least, to bake it to a turn, so that it is neither too hard nor too soft, but just crisp enough. The condition is, the princess must know how to bake gingerbread."

The Lord Chamberlain was terribly frightened on hearing this, but he managed to recover sufficiently to say that, without doubt, a princess could be found who would know how to bake gingerbread.

"Very well," said the king, "suppose we begin the search together."

And that afternoon, in company with the Lord Chamberlain, he visited all the neighboring sovereigns who were known to have spare princesses to give away. Among them all were three who were both wise and beautiful enough to please the king. But, unhappily, none of them could bake gingerbread!

"I cannot bake gingerbread, but I can make the nicest little almond cakes you ever saw," said the first princess, in answer to the king's question. "Won't that do?"

"No, it must be gingerbread," the king said, decidedly.

The second princess, when the king asked her, made up a dreadful face, and said, angrily, "I wish you'd leave me alone, stupid! There is not a princess in the world who can bake gingerbread—gingerbread, indeed!"

The king fared worse when he asked the third princess, though she was the wisest and fairest of all. She gave him no chance to ask his question; even before he had opened his mouth, she demanded if he could play on the trombone. When he acknowledged that he could not, she said that she was really sorry, but that she could not marry him, as he wouldn't suit. She liked him well enough, but she dearly loved to hear the trombone played, and she had decided never to marry any man who couldn't play it.

The king drove home with the Lord Chamberlain, and as he stepped out of the carriage he said, quite discouraged, "So we are about as far in our plans as we were before."

However, as a king must have a queen, after a time he sent for the Lord Chamberlain again, and acknowledged that he had resigned the hope of marrying a princess who could bake gingerbread. "I will marry the princess who can bake nice little almond cakes," he added. "Go, and ask her if she will be my wife."

When the Lord Chamberlain returned, the next day, he told his majesty that the princess was no more to be had, as she had married the king of the country where slate pencils and pickled limes grew.

So the Chamberlain was sent to the second princess, but he came back equally unsuccessful, for the king, her father, regretted to say that his daughter was dead; and that was the end of the second princess.

After this the king pondered a good deal, but as he really wished to have a queen, he commanded the Lord Chamberlain to go to the third princess. "Perhaps she has changed her mind," he thought.

The Lord Chamberlain had to obey, much to his disgust, for even his wife said it was quite useless; and the king awaited his return with great anxiety, for he remembered the question about the trombone, and it was really irritating.

The third princess received the Lord Chamberlain very graciously, and remarked that she had once decided never to marry a man who could not play on the trombone. But that was a dream—a youthful, idle dream, she sighed, a hope never to be realized—and as she liked the king in spite of this drawback, why—she would marry him.

The Lord Chamberlain whipped up his horses and tore down the road to the palace, where the King, overjoyed at the good tidings, embraced his faithful servant and gave him as reward all sorts of toy crosses, and stars to wear at

193

his breast, and about fifteen yards of ribbon to wind about his neck and shoulders.

The wedding was splendid. The whole city was gay with flags and banners, and garlands hung in huge festoons from house to house; and for two whole weeks nothing else was thought of and talked about.

The king and queen lived so happily together for a year that the king had quite forgotten about the gingerbread and the queen about the trombone. Unhappily, one morning, the king got out of bed with his left foot foremost, and that day all things went wrong. It rained from morning till night; the royal crown tumbled down and smashed the cross on top; besides, the court painter who brought the new map of the kingdom had made a mistake and colored the country red, instead of blue, as the king had commanded; lastly, the queen had a headache. So it happened that the royal pair quarreled for the first time, though they could not have told the reason why. In short, the king was cross, and the queen was snappish and insisted on having the last word.

"It is about time that you ceased finding fault with everything," the queen said at last, with great scorn. "Why, you can't even play on the trombone."

"And you can't bake gingerbread," the king retorted, quick as a flash.

For the first time the queen did not know what to say, and so, without another word, they went to their separate rooms. The queen threw herself on the sofa and wept bitterly. "What a little fool you are!" she sobbed. "Where was your common sense? You couldn't have been more stupid if you had tried."

As for the king, he strode up and down the room rubbing his hands. "It is fortunate that my wife can't bake gingerbread," he thought, gleefully, "for if she could, what should I have answered when she said that I couldn't play on the trombone?"

The more he thought, the more cheerful he became. He whistled a favorite tune, looked at the great picture of his wife over the mantle, and then, climbing upon a chair, he brushed away a cobweb that was dangling over the nose of the queen.

"How angry she must have been, poor little woman!" he said at last. "Suppose I see what she is doing."

He stepped into the long corridor into which all the rooms opened, and it being the day when all things went wrong, the groom of the chambers had forgotten to light the entry lamp, though it was eight o'clock at night and pitch dark. The king went groping forward, with his hands stretched out for fear of falling, when suddenly he touched something very soft.

"Who is there?" he demanded.

"It is I," said the queen.

"What are you in search of, my dear?"

"I wanted to beg your pardon—I was very unkind," she sobbed.

"Pray don't, my love," the king said, in his very gentlest tone of voice. "It was my fault, but all is forgotten. One thing, let me say, however, my dear, there are two words which must never be uttered in our kingdom on pain of death—"trombone' and —"

"Gingerbread," the queen added, laughing, though she stealthily brushed away a tear.

And so the story ends.

What the Goodman Does Is Always Right

Adapted from the story by Hans Christian Ander-
sen.   10 minutes

I will tell you a story which was told to me when
I was a little boy. Every time I think of the story, it
seems to me to become more and more charming; for it
is with stories as with many people—they become better
as they grow older.

I take it for granted that you have been in the country,
and have seen a very old farmhouse with a thatched roof,
and mosses and small plants growing wild upon the thatch.
There is a stork's nest on the summit of the gable, for
we can't do without the stork. The walls of the house
are sloping, and the windows are low, and only one of the
latter is made so it will open. The baking oven sticks out
of the wall like a little fat body. The elder tree hangs
over the paling, and beneath its branches, at the foot of
the paling, is a pool of water in which a few ducks are
disporting themselves. There is a yard dog, too, who barks
at all comers.

Just such a farmhouse stood out in the country, and in
this house dwelt on old couple—a man and his wife. Small
as was their property, there was one thing that they could
do without—a horse, which lived on the grass it found
by the side of the high-road. The old farmer rode into the
town on this horse, and often his neighbors borrowed it
from him, and rendered the couple some service in return.
But they thought it would be best if they sold the horse,

or exchanged it for something that might be more useful to them. But what might this something be?

"You'll know that best, goodman," said his wife. "It is fair day today, so ride into town, and get rid of the horse for money, or make a good exchange. Whatever you do is sure to be right."

And she fastened his neckerchief for him, for she could do that better than he could; and she tied it in a double bow, for she could do that very prettily. Then she brushed his hat round and round with the palm of her hand, and gave him a kiss. So he rode away upon the horse that was to be sold or bartered for something else. Yes, the goodman knew what he was about.

The sun shone hotly down, not a cloud was to be seen in the sky. The road was very dusty, for many people who were all bound for the fair were driving, riding, or walking upon it. There was no shelter anywhere from the sun.

Among the rest, was a man trudging along and driving a cow to the fair. The cow was a beautiful creature. "She gives good milk, I'm sure," said the farmer. "That would be a very good exchange—the cow for the horse."

"Hallo, you there with the cow!" he said. "I'll tell you what—I fancy a horse costs more than a cow, but I don't care for that. A cow would be more useful to me. If you like, we'll exchange."

"To be sure I will," said the man, and they exchanged accordingly.

So that was settled, and the farmer might have turned back, for he had done the business he came to do; but as he had once made up his mind to go to the fair, he determined to proceed, merely to have a look at it; so he went on to the town with his cow.

Leading the animal, he strode sturdily on; and after a time he overtook a man who was driving a sheep. It was a good, fat sheep, with a fine fleece on its back.

197

"I should like to have that fellow," said our farmer to himself. "He would find plenty of grass, and in the winter we could keep him in the room with us. Perhaps it would be more practical to have a sheep instead of a cow. Shall we exchange?"

The man with the sheep was quite ready, and the bargain was struck. So the farmer went on in the high-road with his sheep.

Soon he overtook another man, who came into the road from a field, carrying a great goose under his arm.

"That's a heavy thing you have there. It has plenty of feathers and plenty of fat, and would look well tied to a string and paddling in the water at our place. That would be something for my wife; she could make all kinds of profit out of it. How often has she said, 'If we only had a goose!' Now, perhaps she can have one, and, if possible, it shall be hers. Shall we exchange? I'll give you my sheep for your goose, and thank you into the bargain."

The other man had not the least objection; and accordingly they exchanged, and our farmer became proprietor of the goose.

By this time he was very near the town. The crowd on the high road became greater and greater; there was quite a crush of men and cattle. They walked in the road, and at the barrier they even walked into the toll-man's potato field, where his one hen was strutting about, with a string to its leg, lest it should take fright at the crowd, and stray away, and so be lost. This hen had short tail feathers, and winked with both its eyes, and looked very cunning. "Cluck, cluck!" said the hen. What it thought when it said this I cannot tell you; but as soon as our goodman saw it, he thought, "That's the finest hen I've ever seen in my life! Why, it's finer than our parson's brood hen. On my word, I should like to have it. A hen can always find a grain or two, and can almost keep

198

itself. I think it would be a good exchange if I could get that for my goose."

"Shall we exchange?" he asked the toll taker.

"Exchange!" repeated the man. "Well, that would not be a bad thing."

And so they exchanged; the toll taker at the barrier kept the goose, and the farmer carried away the hen.

Now, he had done a good deal of business on his way to the fair, and he was hot and tired. He wanted something to eat and something to drink; and soon he was in front of the inn. He was just about to step in when the hostler came out, so they met at the door. The hostler was carrying a sack.

"What have you in that sack?" asked the farmer.

"Rotten apples," answered the hostler, "a whole sackful of them—enough to feed the pigs."

"Why, that's terrible waste! I should like to take them to my wife at home. Last year the old tree by the turf hole only bore a single apple, and we kept it in the cupboard till it was quite rotten and spoilt. 'It was always property,' my wife said. But here she could see a quantity of property—a whole sackful. Yes, I shall be glad to show them to her."

"What will you give me for the sackful?" asked the hostler.

"What will I give? I will give my hen in exchange."

And he gave the hen accordingly, and received the apples, which he carried into the guest room. He leaned the sack carefully by the stove, and then went to the table. But the stove was hot; he had not thought of that. Many guests were present—horse dealers, ox herders, and two Englishmen.

Hiss-s-s! hiss-s-s! What was that by the stove? The apples were beginning to roast!

"Why, do you know—" said our farmer. And he told the whole story of the horse he had exchanged for a cow, and all the rest of it, down to the apples.

"Well, your wife will give it to you well when you get home!" said one of the Englishmen. "There will be a disturbance."

"What?—give me what?" said the farmer. "She will kiss me, and say, 'What the goodman does is always right.'"

"Shall we wager?" said the Englishman. "We'll wager coined gold by the ton—a hundred pounds to the hundred weight!"

"A bushel will be enough," replied the farmer. "I can only set the bushel of apples against it; and I'll throw myself and my wife into the bargain—and I fancy that's piling up the measure."

"Done—taken!"

And the bet was made. The host's carriage came up, and the Englishmen got in, and the peasant got in; away they went, and soon they stopped before the farmer's hut.

"Good evening, wife."

"Good evening, goodman."

"I've made the exchange."

"Yes, you understand what you're about," said the woman.

And she embraced him, and paid no attention to the stranger guests nor did she notice the sack.

"I got a cow in exchange for the horse," said he.

"Heaven be thanked!" said she. "What glorious milk we shall have, and butter and cheese on the table! That was a capital exchange."

"Yes, but I changed the cow for a sheep."

"Ah, that's better still!" cried the wife. "You always think of everything; we have just pasture enough for a sheep. Ewe's milk and cheese, and woolen jackets and stockings! The cow cannot give those, and her hairs will only come off. How you think of everything!"

200

"But I changed away the sheep for a goose."

"Then this year we shall really have roast goose to eat, my dear man. You are always thinking of something to give me pleasure. How charming this is! We can let the goose walk about with a string to her leg, and she'll grow fatter still before we roast her."

"But I gave away the goose for a hen," said the man.

"A hen? That was a good exchange!" replied the woman. "The hen will lay eggs and hatch them, and we shall have chickens; we shall have a whole poultry yard! Oh, that's just what I was wishing for."

"Yes, but I exchanged the fowl for a sack of shriveled apples."

"What!—I must positively kiss you for that," exclaimed the wife. "My dear, good husband! Now, I'll tell you something. Do you know, you had hardly left me this morning, before I began thinking how I could give you something very nice this evening. I thought it should be pancakes with savory herbs. I had eggs and bacon, too; but I wanted herbs. So I went to the schoolmaster's and begged his wife to lend me a handful of herbs. 'Lend!' she answered me; 'nothing at all grows in our garden, not even a shriveled apple. I could not even lend you a shriveled apple, my dear woman.' But now I can lend her ten, or a whole sackful. That I'm very glad of; that makes me laugh!" And with that she gave him a sounding kiss.

"I like that!" exclaimed both the Englishmen together. "Always going down hill, and always merry; that's worth the money." So they paid a hundredweight of gold to the farmer who was not scolded, but kissed.

Yes, it always pays, when the wife sees and always asserts that her husband knows best, and that whatever he does is right.

You see, that is my story, I heard it when I was a child; and now you have heard it too, and know that "What the goodman does is always right."

Indian

The Legend of Scarface

Adapted from *Blackfoot Lodge Tales* by George
Bird Grinnell.   15 minutes

Once when there were no wars among the Indians and
all the tribes were at peace, there was an Indian man who
had a very beautiful daughter. Many young men wanted
to marry her, but everytime she was asked, she only shook
her head and said she did not want a husband.

"How is this?" asked her father. "Some of these young
men are rich, handsome and brave."

"Why should I marry?" replied the girl. "I have a rich
father and mother. Our lodge is good. There are plenty
of tanned robes and soft furs for winter. Why worry me
then?"

One day the Raven Bearers of the tribe held a dance;
they all dressed carefully and wore their ornaments, and
each one tried to dance the best. Afterward some of them
asked for this girl, but still she said no. Then her father
was angry and said, "Why, now, this way? All the best
men have asked for you, and still you say no."

"Father! Mother!" replied the girl. "Pity me. Now
hear the truth. That Above Person, the Sun, told me, 'Do
not marry any of those men, for you are mine. Thus shall
you be happy, and live to great age."

"Ah," replied her father. "It must always be as he
says." And they talked no more about it.

There was a young man, very poor. His father, mother,
all his relations had gone to the Sand Hills. He had no
lodge, no wife to tan his robes or sew his moccasins. He
was a good looking young man, except that he had a scar
on his cheek.

After one of the dances some of the young men met this poor Scarface and they laughed at him, and said, "Why don't *you* ask that girl to marry you? You are so rich and handsome!" Scarface did not laugh. He replied "Ah, I will do as you say. I will go and ask her." All the young men thought this was very funny. But Scarface went down by the river. He waited where the young women came to get water, and by and by the girl came along. "Girl," he said, "wait. I want to speak with you."

"Speak then," said the girl.

"I have seen the days," continued the young man "that you have refused those who are young, and rich, and brave. Now, today, they laughed and said to me, 'Why do you not ask her?' I am poor, very poor. I have no lodge, no food, no clothes, no robes and warm furs. I have no relations; all have gone to the Sand Hills; yet now, today, I ask you, take pity, be my wife."

The girl hid her face in her robe. After a time she said, "True, I have refused all those rich young men, and yet now the poor one asks me, and I am glad. I will be your wife, and my people will be happy. You are poor, but it does not matter. My father will give you dogs. My mother will make us a lodge. My people will give us robes and furs. You will be poor no longer."

Then the young man was happy, and he started to kiss her, but she held him back, and said, "Wait! The Sun has spoken to me. He says I may not marry; that I belong to him. He says if I listen to him, I shall live to a great age. So now I say, go to the Sun. Tell him, 'She whom you spoke with heeds your words, but now she wants to marry. I want her for my wife.' Ask him to take that scar from your face. That will be his sign. I will know he is pleased. But if he refuses, or if you fail to find his lodge, then do not return to me."

"Oh!" cried the young man. "At first your words were good. I was glad. But now it is dark. My heart is dead.

Where is that far-off lodge? Where is the trail which no one yet has traveled?"

"Take courage, take courage!" said the girl, and she went to her lodge.

Scarface was very sad. He sat down and covered his head with his robe and tried to think what to do. After a while he got up and went to an old woman who had been kind to him.

"Pity me," he said, "I am very poor. I am going away now on a long journey. Make me some moccasins."

"Where are you going?" asked the old woman. "There is no war. We are very peaceful here."

"I do not know where I shall go," replied Scarface. "I am in trouble, but I cannot tell you now what it is." So the old woman made him some moccasins, seven pairs, and also gave him a sack of food—for she had a good heart, and she liked the young man.

All alone, and with a sad heart, he climbed the bluffs and stopped to take a last look at the camp. He wondered if he would ever see his sweetheart and the people again.

"Pity me, O Sun," he prayed, and turning, he started to look for the trail.

For many days he traveled on, over great prairies and among the mountains. One night he stopped by the home of a wolf.

"What is my brother doing so far from home?" asked the wolf.

"Ah!" replied Scarface. "I seek the place where the Sun lives; I am sent to speak with him."

"I have traveled far," said the wolf. "But I have never seen the Sun's home. Wait; I know one who is very wise. Ask the bear. He may tell you."

The next day the man traveled on again, and when night came he arrived at the bear's lodge.

"Where is your home?" asked the bear. "Why are you traveling alone, my brother?"

"Help me! Pity me!" replied the young man. "Because of a maiden's words I seek the Sun. I go to ask him for her."

"I know not where he stops," replied the bear. "I have traveled by many rivers, and I know the mountains, yet I have never seen his lodge. There is someone beyond, that striped-face badger who is very smart. Go and ask him."

The badger was in his hole. Stooping over, the young man shouted, "O cunning striped-face! I wish to speak with you."

"What do you want?" said the badger.

"I want to find the Sun's home," replied Scarface. "I want to speak with him."

"I do not know where he lives," replied the badger. "I never travel very far. Over there in the timber is a wolverine. Maybe he can tell you."

Then Scarface went to the woods and looked all around for the wolverine, but could not find him. So he sat down to rest.

"Hai-yu! Hai-yu!" he cried. "Wolverine, take pity on me. My food is gone, my moccasins worn out. Now I must die."

"What is it, my brother?" he heard, and looking around, he saw the animal sitting near.

"She whom I would marry," said Scarface, "belongs to the Sun; I am trying to find where he lives, to ask him for her."

"Ah," said the wolverine, "I know where he lives. Wait; it is nearly night. Tomorrow I will show you the trail to the big water. He lives on the other side of it."

Early in the morning the wolverine showed him the trail, and Scarface followed it until he came to the water's edge. The other side could not be seen, it was so wide. Scarface sat down on the shore. His food was all gone, his moccasins worn out. His heart was sick. "I cannot cross this big

208

water," he said. "I cannot return to the people. Here, by this water, I shall die."

Two swans came swimming up to the shore. "Why have you come here?" they asked him. "What are you doing? It is very far to the place where your people live."

"I am here," replied Scarface, "to die. Far away, in my country, is a beautiful girl. I want to marry her, but she belongs to the Sun. So I started to find him and ask for her. I have traveled many days. My food is gone. I cannot go back. I cannot cross this big water, so I am going to die."

"No," said the swans. "It shall not be so. Across this water is the home of the Above Person. Get on our backs and we will take you there."

Scarface quickly rose. He felt strong again. He waded out into the water and lay down on the swans' backs, and they started off. The swans carried him safely to the other side. Here was a broad, hard trail leading back from the water's edge.

"Now," said the swans, "you are close to the Sun's lodge. Follow that trail, and you will soon see it."

Scarface started up the trail, and pretty soon he came to some beautiful things lying in it. There was a war shirt, a shield, a bow and arrows. He had never seen such pretty weapons, but he did not touch them. He walked carefully around them and traveled on. A little way farther on, he met a young man, the handsomest person he had ever seen. His hair was very long, and he wore clothing made of strange skins. His moccasins were sewn with bright colored feathers. The young man said to him, "Did you see some weapons lying on the trail?"

"Yes," replied Scarface; "I saw them."

"But did you not touch them?" asked the young man.

"No; I thought some one had left them there, so I did not take them."

209

"You are not a thief," said the young man. "What is your name?"

"Scarface."

"Where are you going?"

"To the Sun."

"My name," said the young man, "is Morning Star. The Sun is my father; come, I will take you to our lodge. My father is not at home, but he will come in at night." Soon they came to the lodge. It was very large and handsome; strange medicine animals were painted on it. Scarface was ashamed to go in, but Morning Star said, "Do not be afraid, my friend; we are glad you have come."

One person was sitting there, the Moon, Morning Star's mother. She spoke to Scarface kindly, and gave him something to eat. "Why have you come so far from your people?" she asked.

Then Scarface told her about the beautiful girl he wanted to marry. "She belongs to the Sun," he said. "I have come to ask him for her."

When it was time for the Sun to come home, the Moon hid Scarface. As soon as the Sun got to the doorway, he stopped, and said, "I smell a person."

"Yes, father," said Morning Star; "a good young man has come to see you. I know he is good, for he found some of my things on the trail and did not touch them."

Then Scarface came out from under the robes, and the Sun entered and sat down. "I am glad you have come to our lodge," he said. "Stay with us as long as you think best. My son is lonesome sometimes; be his friend."

The next day the Moon called Scarface out of the lodge and said to him, "Go with Morning Star where you please, but never hunt near that big water; do not let him go there. It is the home of great birds which have long, sharp bills; they kill people. I have had many sons, but these birds have killed them all. Morning Star is the only one left."

So Scarface stayed there a long time and hunted with Morning Star. One day they came near the water and saw the big birds.

"Come," said Morning Star, "let us go and kill those birds."

"No, no!" replied Scarface. "We must not go there. Those are very terrible birds. They will kill us."

Morning Star would not listen. He ran toward the water, and Scarface followed. He knew that he must kill the birds and save the boy. If not, the Sun would be angry and might kill him. He ran ahead and met the birds, which were coming toward him to fight, and killed every one of them with his spear. Not one was left. Then the young men cut off their heads and carried them home. Morning Star's mother was glad when they told her what they had done and showed her the birds' heads. She cried, and called Scarface "my son." When the Sun came home at night, she told him about it, and he too was glad. "My son," he said to Scarface, "I will not forget what you have done. Tell me now, what can I do for you?"

"Pity me," replied Scarface, "I am here to ask for the girl I want to marry. I asked her, and she was glad; but she says you own her, that you told her not to marry."

"What you say is true," said the Sun. "Now, then, I give her to you; she is yours. Let me tell you something. Be wise, and listen; I am the only chief. Everything is mine. I made the earth, the mountains, prairies, rivers and forests. I made the people and all the animals. This is why I say I alone am the chief. I can never die. True, the winter makes me old and weak, but the summer makes me grow young again." Then said the Sun, "Come with me and see the world."

He took Scarface to the edge of the sky, and they looked down and saw it.

Then he told Scarface everything about making a Medicine Lodge, and when he had finished, he rubbed a power-

211

ful medicine on his face, and the scar disappeared. Then he gave him two raven feathers, saying, "These are the sign for the girl, that I give her to you. They must always be worn by the husband of the woman who builds a Medicine Lodge."

The young man was now ready to return home. Morning Star and the Sun gave him many beautiful presents. The Moon cried and kissed him, and called him "my son." Then the Sun showed him the short trail. It was the Wolf Road—the Milky Way. He followed it, and soon reached the ground.

It was a very hot day. All the lodge skins were raised, and the people sat in the shade. There was a chief, a very generous man, and all day long people kept coming to his lodge to feast and smoke with him. Early in the morning this chief saw a person sitting near by, closely wrapped in his robe. When it was almost night, the chief said, "Why does this person sit there so long? The heat has been strong, but he has neither eaten nor drunk. He may be a stranger; go and ask him in."

So some young men went up to Scarface and said, "Why do you sit here in the great heat all day? Come to the shade of the lodge. The chief asks you to feast with him."

Then Scarface arose and threw off his robe, and they were surprised. He wore beautiful clothes. His bow, shield, and other weapons were of strange make. But they knew his face, although the scar was gone, and they ran ahead, shouting, "The scarface poor young man has come. He is no longer poor. The scar on his face is gone."

All the people rushed out to see him. "Where have you been?" they asked. "Where did you get all those pretty things?"

He did not answer. There in the crowd stood the young maiden; and taking the two raven feathers from his head, he gave them to her, and said, "The trail was very long, and I nearly died, but by the aid of many helpers, I found

212

the lodge of the Sun. He is glad. He sends these feathers to you. They are the sign."

Great was her gladness then. They were married, and made the first Medicine Lodge, as the Sun had said. The Sun was glad. He gave them great age. They were never sick. When they were very old, one morning their children said, "Awake! Rise and eat." They did not move. In the night, in sleep, without pain, their shadows had departed for the Sand Hills.

Myths and Legends

How Theseus Slew the Minotaur

Adapted from *Heroes; Old Greek Fairy Tales for My Children* by Charles Kingsley.   13 minutes

Now you must know that Theseus had been brought up in a distant place and had not been long in his father's country, and did not know why when the spring drew near, all the Athenians grew sad and silent. Theseus saw it, and asked the reason, but no one would answer him a word.

Then he went to his father, and asked him, but Aegeus turned away his face and wept.

"Do not ask, my son, beforehand, about evils which must happen; it is enough to have to face them when they come."

When the spring came, a herald came to Athens, and stood in the market, and cried, "O people and King of Athens, where is your yearly tribute?"

Then a great lamentation arose throughout the city. But Theseus stood up to the herald, and cried, "And who are you, dog faced, who dare demand tribute here? If I did not reverence your herald's staff, I would brain you with this club."

And the herald answered proudly, for he was a grave and ancient man, "Fair youth, I am not dog faced or shameless, for I do the bidding of Minos, my master, the king of hundred-citied Crete. He is the wisest of all kings on earth. And you must surely be a stranger here, or you would know why I come, and that I come by right."

"I am a stranger here. Tell me, then, why you come."

"To fetch the tribute which King Aegeus promised to Minos, and confirmed his promise with an oath. For Minos

217

conquered all this land, when he came hither with a great fleet of ships, enraged about the murder of his son. For his son Androgeos came hither to the games, and overcame all the Greeks in the sports, so that the people honored him as a hero.

"But when Aegeus saw his valor, he envied him, and feared lest he should join the sons of Pallas, and take away the scepter from him. So he plotted against his life, and slew him basely, no man knows how or where. Some say that he waylaid him on the road which goes to Thebes; and some, that he sent him against the bull of Marathon, that the beast might kill him. But Aegeus says that the young men killed him from envy, because he had conquered them in the games. So Minos came hither and avenged him, and would not depart till this land had promised him tribute, seven youths and seven maidens every year, who go with him in a black-sailed ship, till they come to hundred-citied Crete."

And Theseus ground his teeth together, and said, "Wert thou not a herald I would kill thee, for saying such things of my father. I will go to him, and know the truth." So he went to his father, and asked him; but Aegeus turned away his head and wept, and said, "Blood was shed in the land unjustly, and by blood it is avenged. Break not my heart by questions; it is enough to endure in silence."

Then Theseus groaned inwardly, and said, "I will go myself with these youths and maidens, and kill Minos upon his royal throne."

And Aegeus shrieked, and cried, "You shall not go, my son, the light of my old age, to whom alone I look to rule this people after I am dead and gone. You shall not go, to die horribly, as those youths and maidens die; for Minos thrusts them into a labyrinth.

"From that labyrinth no one can escape, entangled in its winding ways, before they meet the Minotaur, the monster who feeds upon the flesh of men. There he devours them horribly, and they never see this land again."

Then Theseus grew red, and his ears tingled, and his heart beat loud in his bosom. He stood awhile like a tall stone pillar on the cliffs above some hero's grave, and at last he spoke,

"Therefore all the more will I go with them, and slay the accursed beast. Have I not slain all evil doers and monsters, that I might free this land? Where are the fifty sons of Pallas? This Minotaur shall go the road which they have gone, and Minos himself, if he dare stay me."

"But how will you slay him, my son? For you must leave your club and your armor behind, and be cast to the monster defenseless and naked like the rest."

And Theseus said, "Are there no stones in that labyrinth? and have I not fists and teeth?"

Then Aegeus clung to Theseus' knees, but he would not listen. At last Aegeus let him go, weeping bitterly.

And Theseus went out to the marketplace where the herald stood, while they drew lots for the youths and maidens who were to sail in that doleful crew.

The people stood wailing and weeping, as the lot fell on this one and on that. But Theseus strode into the midst, and cried,

"Here is a youth who needs no lot. I myself will be one of the seven."

And the herald asked in wonder, "Fair youth, know you whither you are going?"

Theseus said, "I know. Let us go down to the black-sailed ship."

So they went down to the black-sailed ship; seven maidens and seven youths, and Theseus before them all, and the people following them lamenting.

But Theseus whispered to his companions, "Have hope, for the monster is not immortal." Then their hearts were comforted a little; but they wept as they went on board. The cliffs of Sunium and all the isles of the Aegean Sea rang with the voice of their lamentation as they sailed on toward their deaths in Crete.

And at last they came to Crete, and to the palace of Minos the great king. He was the wisest of all mortal kings, and conquered all the Aegean isles, and his ships were as many as the seagulls, and his palace like a marble hill. He sat among the pillars of the hall, upon his throne of beaten gold.

Theseus stood before Minos, and they looked each other in the face. Minos bade his courtiers take them to prison, and cast them to the monster one by one, that the death of Androgeos might be avenged.

Then Theseus cried, "A boon, O Minos! Let me be thrown first to the beast; for I came hither for that very purpose, of my own will, and not by lot."

"Who art thou, then, brave youth?"

"I am the son of him whom of all men thou hatest most, Aegeus, the king of Athens, and I am come here to end this matter."

And Minos pondered awhile, looking steadfastly at him, and he thought, "The lad means to atone by his own death, for his father's sin," and he answered at last, mildly, "Go back in peace, my son. It is a pity that one so brave should die."

But Theseus said, "I have sworn that I will not go back till I have seen the monster face to face."

And at that Minos frowned, and said, "Then thou shalt see him. Take the madman away."

And they led Theseus away into the prison with the other youths and maids.

But Ariadne, King Minos' daughter, saw him as she came out of her white stone hall; and she loved him for his courage and his majesty, and said, "Shame that such a youth should die!"

And by night she went down to the prison, and told him all that was in her heart, and said, "Flee down to your ship at once, for I have bribed the guards before the door. Flee, you and all your friends, and go back in peace to Greece; and take me, take me with you! For I dare not stay after you are gone, for my father will kill me miserably if he knows what I have done."

Theseus stood silent awhile, for he was astonished and confounded by her beauty; but at last he said, "I cannot go home in peace, till I have seen and slain this Minotaur, and avenged the deaths of the youths and maidens, and put an end to the terrors of my land."

"And will you kill the Minotaur? How, then?"

"I know not, nor do I care; but he must be strong, if he be too strong for me."

Then she loved him all the more, and said, "But when you have killed him, how will you find your way out of the labyrinth?"

"I know not, neither do I care; but it must be a strange road, if I do not find it out before I have eaten up the monster's carcass."

Then she loved him all the more, and said, "Fair youth, you are too bold, but I can help you, weak as I am. I will give you a sword, and with that perhaps you may slay the beast; and a ball of silk thread, and by that perhaps you may find your way out again. Only promise me, that if you escape safely, you will take me home with you to Greece; for my father will surely kill me, if he knows what I have done."

Then Theseus laughed, and said, "Am I not safe enough now?" He hid his sword in his bosom, and rolled up the silk in his hand; and then he swore to Ariadne, and fell down before her, and kissed her hands and her feet. She wept over him a long while, and then went away; and Theseus lay down and slept sweetly.

And when the morning came, the guards came in, and led him away to the labyrinth.

And he went down into that doleful gulf, through winding paths among the rocks, under caverns and arches, and over heaps of fallen stone. He turned on the left hand, and on the right hand, and went up and down, till his head was dizzy, but all the while he held his ball of silk thread. For when he went in he had fastened it to a stone, and left it to unroll out of his hand as he went on; and it lasted him till he met the Minotaur in a narrow chasm between black cliffs.

And when he saw the Minotaur he stopped awhile, for he had never seen so strange a beast. His body was a man's, his head was the head of a bull, but his teeth were the teeth of a lion, and with them he tore his prey. When he saw Theseus he roared, put his head down, and rushed at him.

But Theseus stepped aside nimbly, and, as he passed by, cut him in the knee; and, ere he could turn in the narrow path, he followed him, and stabbed him again and again from behind, till the monster fled, bellowing wildly; for he never before had felt a wound. And Theseus followed him at full speed, holding the ball of thread in his left hand.

Then on, through cavern after cavern, under dark ribs of sounding stone, and up rough glens to the edge of the eternal snow, went they, the hunter and the hunted, while the hills bellowed to the monster's bellow.

At last Theseus came up with him, where he lay panting on a slab in the snow, and catching him by the horns, drove the keen sword through his throat.

Then he turned, and went back limping and weary, feeling his way down by the ball of silk till he came to the mouth of that doleful place, and saw Ariadne waiting for him, and whispered, "It is done!" Laying a finger on her lips, she led him to the prison, and set all the prisoners free, while the guards lay sleeping heavily, for she had silenced them with wine.

222

Then they fled to their ship together, and leaped on board, and hoisted up the sail. The night lay dark around them, so that they passed through Minos' ships, and escaped all safe to Naxos; and there Ariadne became Theseus' wife.

The Marvel of the Sword

Adapted from *The Book of King Arthur and His Noble Knights,* edited by Mary MacLeod. Published by the J. B. Lippincott Company.   11 minutes

When Uther Pendragon, King of England, died, the country for a long time stood in great danger, for every lord that was mighty gathered his forces, and many wished to be king. For King Uther's own son, Prince Arthur, who should have succeeded him, was but a child, and Merlin, the mighty magician, had hidden him away.

Now a strange thing had happened at Arthur's birth, and this was how it was. Some time before, Merlin had done Uther a great service, on condition that the King should grant him whatever he wished for. This the King swore a solemn oath to do. Then Merlin made him promise that when his child was born it should be delivered to Merlin to bring up as he chose, for this would be to the child's own great advantage. The King had given his promise so he was obliged to agree. Then Merlin said he knew a very true and faithful man, one of King Uther's lords, by name Sir Ector, who had large possessions in many parts of England and Wales, and that the child should be given to him to bring up.

On the night the baby was born, while he was still unchristened, King Uther commanded two knights and two ladies to take the child wrapped in a cloth of gold, and deliver it to a poor man whom they would find waiting at the postern gate of the castle. This poor man was Merlin in disguise, although they did not know it. So the child was delivered unto Merlin and he carried him to Sir Ector, who

224

had a holy man christen him, and named him Arthur. Sir Ector's wife cherished him as her own child.

Within two years King Uther fell sick of a great malady, and for three days and three nights he was speechless. All the barons were in much sorrow, and asked Merlin what was best to be done.

"There is no remedy," said Merlin, "God will have His will. But look ye all, Barons, come before King Uther tomorrow, and God will make him speak."

So the next day, Merlin and all the barons came before the king, and Merlin said aloud to King Uther:

"Sir, after your days shall your son Arthur be king of this realm and all that belongs to it?"

Then Uther Pendragon turned to him and said in hearing of them all: "I give my son Arthur God's blessing and mine, and bid him pray for my soul, and righteously and honourably claim the crown, on forfeiture of my blessing." And with that, King Uther died.

But Arthur was still only a baby, not two years old, and Merlin knew it would be no use yet to proclaim him king, for there were many powerful nobles in England in those days, who were all trying to get the kingdom for themselves, and perhaps they would kill the little prince. So there was much strife and debate in the land for a long time.

When several years had passed, Merlin went to the Archbishop of Canterbury and counseled him to send for all the lords of the realm, and all the gentlemen of arms, that they should come to London at Christmas, to see if God would not show by some miracle who should rightly be king of the realm. So all the lords and gentlemen made themselves ready and came to London, and long before dawn on Christmas Day they were all gathered in the great church of St. Paul's to pray. When the first service was over, there was seen in the churchyard a large stone, four-square, like marble, and in the midst of it was an anvil of steel, a foot high. In this was stuck by the point a beautiful sword, with naked blade, and there were letters written in gold about the sword, which said thus: "WHOSO PULLETH THIS SWORD OUT OF THIS STONE AND ANVIL IS RIGHTLY KING OF ALL ENGLAND."

Then the people marvelled, and told it to the Archbishop.

"I command," said the Archbishop, "that you keep within the church, and pray unto God still; and that no man touch the sword till the service is over!"

So when the prayers in the church were over, all the lords went to behold the stone and the sword; and when they read the writing some of them—such as wished to be king—tried to pull the sword out of the anvil. But not one could make it stir.

"The man is not here that shall achieve the sword," said the Archbishop. "But doubt not God will make him known. But let us provide ten knights, men of good fame, to keep guard over the sword."

So it was ordained, and proclamation was made that every one who wished might try to win the sword. And upon New Year's Day, the Barons arranged to have a great tournament, in which all knights who would joust or tourney might take a part. This was ordained to keep together all the Lords and Commons, for the Archbishop trusted that it would be made known who should win the sword.

On New Year's Day, after church, the Barons rode to the field, some to joust, and some to tourney, and so it happened that Sir Ector, who had large estates near London, came also to the tournament and with him rode Sir Kay, his son, with young Arthur, his foster brother. As they rode, Sir Kay found he had lost his sword, for he had left it at his father's lodging, so he begged young Arthur to go and fetch it for him.

"That I will, gladly," said Arthur and he rode fast away. But when he came to the house, he found no one at home to give him the sword, for everyone had gone to see the jousting. Then Arthur was angry and said to himself: "I will ride to the churchyard, and take the sword with me that sticks in the stone, for my brother, Sir Kay, shall not be without a sword this day."

When he came to the churchyard, he alighted, and tied his horse to the stile, and went to the tent. But he found no knights, who should have been guarding the sword, for they were all away at the joust. Seizing the sword by the handle he lightly and fiercely pulled it out of the stone, then took his horse and rode his way, till he came to Sir Kay his brother, to whom he delivered the sword.

As soon as Sir Kay saw it, he knew well it was the sword of the stone, so he rode to his father Sir Ector, and said: "Sir, lo, here is the sword of the stone, wherefore I must be King of this land." When Sir Ector saw the sword he turned back, and came to the church, and there they all three alighted and went into the church, and he made his son swear truly how he got the sword.

"By my brother Arthur," said Sir Kay, "for he brought it to me."

"How did you get this sword?" said Sir Ector to Arthur. And the boy told him.

"Now," said Sir Ector, "I understand you must be King of this land."

"Wherefore I?" said Arthur, "and for what cause?"

"Sir," said Ector, "because God will have it so; for never man could draw out this sword but he that shall rightly be King. Now let me see whether you can put the sword there as it was, and pull it out again."

"That is no mastery," said Arthur, and he put it back into the stone.

Then Sir Ector tried to pull out the sword and failed; and Sir Kay also pulled with all his might, but it would not move. "Now you shall try," said Sir Ector to Arthur.

"I will, well," said Arthur, and pulled the sword out easily. At this Sir Ector and Sir Kay knelt down on the ground before him.

"Alas," said Arthur, "mine own dear father and brother, why do you kneel to me?"

"Nay, nay, my lord Arthur, it is not so; I was never your father, nor of your blood; but I know well you are of higher blood than I thought you were." Then Sir Ector told him all, how he had taken him to bring up, and by whose command; and how he had received him from Merlin. And when he understood that Ector was not his father, Arthur was deeply grieved.

"Will you be my good, gracious lord, when you are King?" asked the knight.

"If not, I should be to blame," said Arthur. "For you are the man in the world that I am most beholden to, and my good lady and mother your wife, who has fostered and kept me as well as her own children. And if ever it be God's will that I be King, as you say, you shall desire of me what I shall do, and I shall not fail you; God forbid I should fail you."

"Sir," said Sir Ector, "I shall ask no more of you but that you will make my son, your foster brother Sir Kay, seneschal of all your lands."

"That shall be done," said Arthur, "and by my faith, never man but he shall have that office while he and I live." Then they went to the Archbishop and told him how the sword was achieved, and by whom. On the Twelfth Day all the Barons came to the stone in the churchyard, so that any who wished might try to win the sword. But not one of them all could take it out, except Arthur. Before all the Lords and Commons there assembled he pulled out the sword, whereupon all the Commons cried out at once, "We will have Arthur for our King!" And Arthur took the sword in his hands, and offered it on the altar where the

Archbishop was, and so he was made knight by the best man there.

After some delay, he was crowned, and there he swore to his Lords and Commons to be a true King, and to govern with true justice from thenceforth all the days of his life.

The Miraculous Pitcher

Adapted from *A Wonder-Book for Girls and Boys*
by Nathaniel Hawthorne.   26 minutes

Part I

One evening, in times long ago, old Philemon and his old wife Baucis sat at their cottage door. They talked together about their garden, and their cow, and their grape vine, which clambered over the cottage wall. But the rude shouts of children and the fierce barking of dogs in the village grew louder and louder.

"Ah, wife," cried Philemon, "I fear some poor traveler is seeking hospitality among our neighbors yonder, and, instead of giving him food and lodging, they have set their dogs at him."

"Well-a-day!" answered old Baucis, "I do wish they felt a little more of kindness for their fellow creatures."

"Those children will never come to any good," said Philemon. "But, as for you and me, so long as Providence affords us a crust of bread, let us be ready to give half to any poor homeless stranger that may come along and need it."

"That's right, husband!" said Baucis. "So we will!"

These old folks were quite poor. Their food was seldom anything but bread, milk, and vegetables, with sometimes a portion of honey from their beehive. But they were two of the kindest old people in the world.

Their cottage stood on a rising ground in a valley. This valley had probably once been the bed of a lake. But, as the waters subsided, men had cultivated the soil, and built houses on it, so that it was now a fertile spot. Never was there a prettier or more fruitful valley. The very sight of the plenty around them should have made the inhabitants kind and gentle, and ready to show their gratitude to Providence by doing good to their fellow creatures.

But the people of this lovely village were not worthy to dwell in such a spot. They would only have laughed, had anybody told them that human beings owe a debt of love to one another, because there is no other method of paying the debt of love and care which all of us owe to Providence. They taught their children to be no better than themselves, and used to clap their hands when they saw the little boys and girls run after some poor stranger, shouting at his heels and pelting him with stones. They kept large and fierce dogs, and whenever a traveler ventured to show himself in the village street, this pack of curs scampered to meet him, barking, snarling, and showing their teeth. This was a very terrible thing to poor travelers, especially when they chanced to be sick, or feeble, or lame, or old. Such persons, if they once knew about these unkind people, would go miles and miles out of their way, rather than try to pass through the village again.

What made the matter worse was that when rich persons came, nobody could be more civil than the inhabitants of the village. They would take off their hats, and make the humblest bows you ever saw. If the children were rude, they were pretty certain to get their ears boxed; and as for the dogs, if a single cur in the pack presumed to yelp, his master instantly beat him with a club, and tied him up without any supper.

So now you understand why old Philemon spoke so sorrowfully, when he heard the shouts of the children and the barking of the dogs.

"I never heard the dogs so loud!" observed the good old man.

"Nor the children so rude!" answered his good old wife.

They sat shaking their heads while the noise came nearer and nearer; until they saw two travelers approaching on foot. Close behind them came the fierce dogs and, a little farther off, ran a crowd of children. Once or twice, the younger of the two men turned about and drove the dogs away with a staff which he carried in his hand. His companion, a very tall person, walked calmly along.

Both of the travelers were very humbly clad and looked as if they might not have money enough in their pockets to pay for a night's lodging.

"Come, wife," said Philemon to Baucis, "let us go and meet these poor people. No doubt, they feel almost too heavy hearted to climb the hill."

"Go you and meet them," answered Baucis, "while I make haste within doors, and see whether we can get them anything for supper. A comfortable bowl of bread and milk would do wonders towards raising their spirits."

She hastened into the cottage, while Philemon went forward and extended his hand, saying "Welcome, strangers, welcome!"

"Thank you!" replied the younger of the two. "This is quite another greeting than we have met with yonder in the village. Pray, why do you live in such a neighborhood?"

"Ah!" observed old Philemon, "Providence put me here, I hope, among other reasons, that I may make you what amends I can for the inhospitality of my neighbors."

"Well said, old father!" cried the traveler, laughing.

Philemon was glad to see him in such good spirits, nor would you have fancied, by the traveler's look and manner, that he was weary with a long day's journey, besides being disheartened by rough treatment at the end of it. He was dressed in rather an odd way, with a sort of cap on his head, the brim of which stuck out over both ears. Though it was a summer evening, he wore a cloak, which he kept wrapt closely about him, perhaps because his clothes were shabby. Philemon perceived, too, that he had on a singular

232

pair of shoes; but, as it was now growing dusk, and as the old man's eyesight was none the sharpest, he could not precisely tell in what the strangeness consisted. One thing, certainly, seemed queer. The traveler was so light and active, that it appeared as if his feet sometimes rose from the ground of their own accord, or could only be kept down by an effort.

"I used to be light footed, in my youth," said Philemon to the traveler. "But I always found my feet grew heavier towards nightfall."

"There is nothing like a good staff to help one along," answered the stranger; "and I happen to have an excellent one, as you see."

This staff was the oddest looking staff that Philemon had ever beheld. It was made of olive wood, and had something like a little pair of wings near the top. Two snakes, carved in the wood, were represented as twining themselves about the staff.

By this time, Philemon and his two guests had reached the cottage door.

"Friends," said the old man, "sit down and rest yourselves. My good wife Baucis has gone to see what you can have for supper. We are poor folks, but you shall be welcome to whatever we have in the cupboard."

The younger stranger threw himself carelessly on the bench letting his staff fall. And here happened something marvelous. The staff seemed to get up from the ground of its own accord, and spreading its little pair of wings, it half hopped, half flew, and leaned itself against the wall of the cottage. There it stood quite still, except that the snakes continued to wriggle. But perhaps old Philemon's eyesight had been playing him tricks.

Before he could ask any questions, the elder stranger spoke in a deep tone of voice. "Was there not," he asked, "a lake, in very ancient times, covering the spot where now stands yonder village?"

"Not in my day, friend," answered Philemon. "There were always the fields and meadows, and the old trees, and the little stream murmuring through the midst of the valley. My father, nor his father before him, ever saw it otherwise, and doubtless it will still be the same, when old Philemon shall be gone and forgotten."

"That is more than can be safely foretold," observed the stranger. "Since the villagers have forgotten the affections and sympathies of their nature, it were better that the lake should be rippling over their dwellings again!"

The traveler looked so stern that Philemon was really frightened. The twilight seemed suddenly to grow darker and there was a roll as of thunder in the air. But, in a moment afterwards, the stranger's face became so kindly and mild the old man quite forgot his terror. Nevertheless, he could not help feeling that this elder traveler must be no ordinary personage, perhaps some exceedingly wise man, who went about the world despising wealth and all worldly objects.

While Baucis was getting the supper, the travelers both began to talk with Philemon. The younger made such shrewd and witty remarks that the good old man continually burst out a-laughing, and pronounced him the merriest fellow whom he had seen for many a day.

"Pray, my young friend," said he, as they grew familiar together, "what may I call your name?"

"Why, I am very nimble, as you see," answered the traveler. "So, if you call me Quicksilver, the name will fit tolerably well."

"Quicksilver? Quicksilver?" repeated Philemon, looking in the traveler's face, to see if he were making fun of him. "It is a very odd name! And your companion there? Has he as strange a one?"

"You must ask the thunder!" replied Quicksilver, putting on a mysterious look. "No other voice is loud enough."

234

When the elder stranger conversed, it was with gravity, and in such a way that Philemon felt moved to tell him everything which he had most at heart.

But Philemon had not many secrets to disclose. He talked about the events of his past life. He and his wife had dwelt in the cottage from their youth upward, earning their bread by honest labor, always poor, but still contented. Because they loved one another so very much, it was the wish of both that death might not separate them, but that they should die, as they had lived, together.

As the stranger listened, a smile beamed over his countenance. "You are a good old man," said he, "and you have a good old wife. It is fit that your wish be granted."

Baucis had now got supper ready, and coming to the door, began to make apologies. "Had we known you were coming," said she, "my good man and I would have gone without a morsel, rather than you should lack a better supper. But I took the most of today's milk to make cheese; and our last loaf is already half eaten. Ah me! I never feel the sorrow of being poor, save when a poor traveler knocks at our door."

"Do not trouble yourself, my good dame," replied the elder stranger, kindly. "An honest, hearty welcome works miracles with the fare."

"A welcome you shall have," cried Baucis, "and likewise a little honey that we happened to have left, and a bunch of purple grapes besides."

"Why, Mother Baucis, it is a feast!" exclaimed Quicksilver, laughing, "and you shall see how bravely I will play my part at it! I think I never felt hungrier in my life."

"Mercy on us!" whispered Baucis to her husband. "I am afraid there will not be half enough supper!"

Then they all went into the cottage.

Now Quicksilver's staff had set itself up against the wall of the cottage and when its master entered the door, leaving it behind, what should it do but immediately spread its little wings, and go hopping and fluttering up the doorsteps! Tap, tap, went the staff, on the kitchen floor; nor did it rest until it had stood itself on end beside Quicksilver's chair. Old Philemon and his wife were so taken up in attending to their guests, that no notice was given to what the staff had been doing.

Part II

There was but a scanty supper for two hungry travelers. In the middle of the table was the remnant of a brown loaf, with a piece of cheese on one side of it, and a dish of honeycomb on the other. There was a pretty good bunch of grapes for each of the guests. A moderate sized earthen pitcher, nearly full of milk, stood at a corner of the board; and when Baucis had filled two bowls, and set them before the strangers, only a little milk remained in the bottom of the pitcher. Baucis kept wishing that she might starve for a week to come in order to provide these hungry folks with a more plentiful supper.

And, since the supper was so exceedingly small, she could not help wishing that their appetites had not been quite so large. For the travelers both drank off all the milk in their two bowls, at a draught.

"A little more milk, kind Mother Baucis, if you please," said Quicksilver. "The day has been hot, and I am very much athirst."

"My dear people," answered Baucis, "I am so sorry and ashamed! But the truth is, there is hardly a drop more milk in the pitcher. O husband! why didn't we go without our supper?"

"Why, it appears to me," cried Quicksilver, starting up from the table and taking the pitcher by the handle, "it really appears to me that matters are not quite so bad as you represent them. Here is certainly more milk in the pitcher."

So saying he proceeded to fill, not only his own bowl, but his companion's likewise, from the pitcher that was sup-

236

posed to be almost empty. Baucis could scarcely believe her eyes. She had certainly poured out nearly all the milk, and had peeped in afterwards, and seen the bottom of the pitcher, as she set it down upon the table.

"But I am old," thought Baucis to herself, "and apt to be forgetful. I suppose I must have made a mistake."

"What excellent milk!" observed Quicksilver. "Excuse me, my kind hostess, but I really must ask you for a little more."

Now Baucis had seen that Quicksilver had turned the pitcher upside down, and had poured out every drop of milk, in filling the last bowl. There could not possibly be any left. However she lifted the pitcher, and made a gesture as of pouring milk into Quicksilver's bowl, but without the remotest idea that any milk would stream forth. What was her surprise, therefore, when an abundant cascade fell bubbling into the bowl, immediately filled it to the brim and overflowed upon the table!

What a delicious fragrance the milk had! It seemed as if Philemon's only cow must have pastured that day, on the richest herbage that could be found anywhere in the world.

"And now a slice of your brown loaf, Mother Baucis," said Quicksilver, "and a little of that honey!"

Baucis cut him a slice accordingly; and though the loaf, when she and her husband ate of it, had been rather too dry and crusty to be palatable, it was now as light and moist as if but a few hours out of the oven. Tasting a crumb, which had fallen on the table, she found it more delicious than bread ever was before, and could hardly believe that it was a loaf of her own kneading and baking.

But, oh, the honey! Its color was that of the purest and most transparent gold; and it had the odor of a thousand flowers. Never was such honey tasted, seen, or smelt.

Although good Mother Baucis was a simple old dame, she could not but think that there was something rather out of the common way in all that had been going on. So, after helping the guests to bread and honey, and laying a bunch of grapes by each of their plates, she sat down by Philemon and told him in a whisper what she had seen.

"Did you ever hear the like?" asked she.

"No, I never did," answered Philemon, with a smile. "I rather think, my dear old wife, you have been walking about in a sort of dream. If I had poured out the milk, I should have seen through this at once. There happened to be a little more in the pitcher than you thought—that is all."

"Ah, husband," said Baucis, "say what you will, these are very uncommon people."

"Well, well," replied Philemon, still smiling, "perhaps they are."

Each of the guests had now taken his bunch of grapes upon his plate. Baucis was of the opinion that the clusters had grown larger and richer, and that each separate grape seemed to be on the point of bursting with ripe juice.

"Very admirable grapes, these!" observed Quicksilver, as he swallowed one after another, without apparently diminishing his cluster. "Pray, my good host, whence did you gather them?"

"From my own vine," answered Philemon, "But wife and I never thought the grapes very fine ones."

"I never tasted better," said the guest. "Another cup of this delicious milk, if you please, and I shall then have supped better than a prince."

This time old Philemon took up the pitcher; for he was curious to discover whether there was any reality in the marvels which Baucis had whispered to him. She was seldom mistaken in what she supposed to be true, but he wanted to see into it with his own eyes. On taking up the pitcher, he slyly peeped into it, and was fully satisfied that it contained not so much as a single drop. All at once, however, he beheld a little white fountain, which gushed up from the bottom of the pitcher, and speedily filled it to the brim with foaming milk. It was lucky that Philemon, in his surprise, did not drop the miraculous pitcher from his hand.

"Who are ye, wonder-working strangers?" cried he, even more bewildered than his wife had been.

"Your guests, my good Philemon, and your friends," replied the elder traveler. "Give me likewise a cup of the milk; and may your pitcher never be empty for kind Baucis and yourself, any more than for the needy wayfarer!"

The supper being now over, the strangers asked to be shown to their place of repose. The old people would gladly have talked with them a little longer. But the elder traveler had inspired them with such reverence that they dared not ask him any questions. And when Philemon drew Quicksilver aside, and inquired how under the sun a fountain of milk could have got into an old earthen pitcher, he pointed to his staff.

"There is the whole mystery of the affair," quoth Quicksilver; "and if you can make it out, I'll thank you to let me know. I can't tell what to make of my staff. It is always playing such odd tricks as this."

He said no more, but looked so slyly in their faces, that they rather fancied he was laughing at them. The magic staff went hopping at his heels, as Quicksilver quitted the room. When left alone, the good old couple spent some little time in conversation about the events of the evening, and then lay down on the floor, and fell fast asleep.

The old man and his wife were stirring betimes in the morning, and the strangers likewise arose with the sun, and made their preparations to depart. Philemon entreated them to remain a little longer, until Baucis could milk the cow, and bake a cake upon the hearth, and, perhaps, find them a few fresh eggs for breakfast. The guests, however, persisted in setting out immediately, but asked Philemon and Baucis to walk forth with them a short distance, and show them the road which they were to take.

So they all four issued from the cottage, chatting together like old friends.

239

"Ah, me! Well-a-day!" exclaimed Philemon, when they had walked a little way from the door. "If our neighbors only knew what a blessed thing it is to show hospitality to strangers, they would tie up all their dogs, and never allow their children to fling another stone."

"It is a sin and shame for them to behave so," cried Baucis. "And I mean to tell some of them what naughty people they are!"

"I fear," remarked Quicksilver, "that you will find none of them at home. And by the by, my dear old people, where is this same village that you talk about? Methinks I do not see it."

Philemon and his wife turned towards the valley. But to their astonishment there was no longer any village!

The old couple were greatly perplexed, and felt as if they could only have been dreaming about a village having lain there. But the next moment they remembered the vanished dwellings, and the faces and characters of the inhabitants, far too distinctly for a dream. The village had been there yesterday, and now was gone!

"Alas!" cried the kind hearted old people, "what has become of our poor neighbors?"

"They exist no longer as men and women," said the elder traveler, in his grand deep voice.

"As for those foolish people," said Quicksilver, with his mischievous smile, "they are all transformed to fishes. There needed but little change, for they were already a scaly set of rascals, and the coldest blooded beings in existence."

"As for you, good Philemon," continued the elder traveler, "—and you, kind Baucis—you, with your scanty means, have mingled so much heartfelt hospitality with your entertainment of the homeless stranger, that the milk became an inexhaustible fount of nectar, and the brown loaf and the honey were ambrosia. You have done well, my dear old

240

friends. Wherefore, request whatever favor you have most at heart, and it is granted."

Philemon and Baucis looked at one another, and then—I know not which of the two it was who spoke, but that one uttered the desire of both their hearts.

"Let us live together, while we live, and leave the world at the same instant, when we die! For we have always loved one another!"

"Be it so!" replied the stranger, with majestic kindness. "Now, look towards your cottage!"

They did so. But what was their surpise on beholding a tall edifice of white marble, with a wide open portal, occupying the spot where their humble residence had so lately stood!

"There is your home," said the stranger, smiling. "Exercise your hospitality in yonder palace as freely as in the poor hovel to which you welcomed us last evening."

The old folks fell on their knees to thank him; but, behold! neither he nor Quicksilver was there.

So Philemon and Baucis took up their residence in the marble palace, and spent their time in making everybody jolly and comfortable who happened to pass that way. Thus the old couple lived a great, great while and grew older and older, and very old indeed. At length, however, there came a summer morning when Philemon and Baucis failed to make their appearance to invite the guests of over night to breakfast. The guests searched everywhere, and all to no purpose. But, after a great deal of perplexity, they espied, in front of the portal, two venerable trees, which nobody could remember to have seen there the day before. Yet there they stood, with their roots fastened deep into the soil, and a huge breadth of foliage overshadowing the whole front of the edifice. One was an oak, and the other a linden tree. Their boughs—it was strange and beautiful to see—were intertwined together, and embraced one another, so

241

that each tree seemed to live in the other tree's bosom much more than in its own.

While the guests were marveling how these trees, that must have required at least a century to grow, could have come to be so tall and venerable in a single night, a breeze sprang up, and set their intermingled boughs astir. And then there was a deep, broad murmur in the air, as if the two mysterious trees were speaking.

"I am old Philemon!" mumured the oak.

"I am old Baucis!" mumured the linden tree.

But as the breeze grew stronger, the trees both spoke at once, "Philemon! Baucis! Baucis! Philemon!" as if one were both and both were one, and talking together in the depths of their mutual heart. It was plain enough to perceive that the good old couple had renewed their age, and were now to spend a quiet and delightful hundred years or so, Philemon as an oak, and Baucis as a linden tree. And oh, what a hospitable shade did they fling around them. Whenever a wayfarer paused beneath it, he heard a pleasant whisper of the leaves above his head, and wondered how the sound should so much resemble words like these,

"Welcome, welcome, dear traveler, welcome!"

And some kind soul, who knew what would have pleased old Baucis and old Philemon best, built a circular seat around both their trunks, where, for a great while afterwards, the weary, and the hungry, and the thirsty used to repose themselves, and quaff milk abundantly out of the miraculous pitcher.

242

Thanksgiving

The Kingdom of the Greedy

Adapted from the French story by P. J. Stahl.
St. Nicholas, 1876.   15 minutes

The country of the Greedy was ruled by a king who had much trouble. His subjects were well behaved, but they had one sad fault, they were too fond of pies and tarts. This deplorable taste made the fortunes of the pastry cooks.

The King of the Greedy sought long for the means of correcting this passion for sweets.

"Your Majesty," said the great court doctor at his last audience, "your people look like putty! They are incurable. Their senseless love for good eating will bring them all to the grave."

This view of things did not suit the king. He was wise, and saw very plainly that a monarch without subjects would be but a sorry king.

Happily [after this utter failure of the doctors], a fine idea came into the mind of His Majesty. He telegraphed for Mother Mitchel, the most celebrated of all pastry cooks. Mother Mitchel soon arrived, with her black cat, Fanfreluche, who accompanied her everywhere, and inquired what she and her cat could do for His Majesty. The king demanded of the astonished pastry cook a tart as big as the capitol—bigger even, if possible, but no smaller!

The king gave Mother Mitchel one month to carry out his gigantic project. "It is enough," she proudly replied, brandishing her crutch. Then, taking leave of the king, she and her cat set out for their home.

On the way Mother Mitchel arranged in her head the plan of the monumental pastry which was to immortalize her, and considered the means of making it. As to its form and size, it was to be as exact a copy of the capitol as possible, since the king had willed it; but its outside crust should have a beauty all its own. The dome must be adorned with sugarplums of all colors, and topped off with a splendid crown of macaroons, spun sugar, chocolate, and candied fruits. It was no small affair.

Mother Mitchel did not like to lose time. Her plan of battle once formed, she recruited on her way all the little pastry cooks of the country, then called upon all the millers of the land, and commanded them to bring together at a certain time as many sacks of flour as they could grind in a week.

At the call of Mother Mitchel all the farmers' wives went to work; they rushed to the hen coops to collect seven thousand fresh eggs.

The milkmaids were busy from morning till night milking the cows, for she must have twenty thousand pails of milk.

And now she called for a thousand pounds of the best butter. All the churns for twenty miles around began to work in the most lively manner.

On the appointed day all the millers arrived, each laden with a great sack of flour.

All the farmers' wives arrived in turn, with baskets of eggs upon their heads. They did not load their donkeys with them, for fear that in jogging along they would become omelettes on the way. Mother Mitchel had the patience to look through every egg to see if it was fresh.

And now the milkmaids with their pots and pails of milk, and the buttermakers with their baskets filled with the rich yellow pats of butter, filed in long procession to the right and left of the cabin of Mother Mitchel. Then came the grocers, with their aprons of coffee bags. Each one clasped to his heart a sugar loaf nearly as large as himself. From another direction came a whole army of country people, rolling wheelbarrows and carrying huge baskets, all filled with cherries, plums, peaches, and pears. The fruits were all put into bins, each kind by itself. And now the preparations were finished. There was no time to lose before setting to work.

The spot which Mother Mitchel had chosen for her great edifice was a pretty hill which commanded a view of the capital city.

All the ingredients for the tart were now ready. Upon the order of Mother Mitchel they began to peel the apples and pears. Not far away, the children were stoning the plums, cherries, and peaches.

It was then the turn of the ambitious scullery maids to break the seven thousand eggs.

Then began the real labor of Mother Mitchel. First, she had to make sweetmeats and jam out of all the immense quantity of fruit she had stored. For this, as she could only do one kind at a time, she had ten kettles, each as big as a dinner table. During the forty-eight hours the cooking went on, a dozen scullery maids blew the fire and put on the fuel. Mother Mitchel, with a spoon that four modern cooks could hardly lift, never ceased stirring and trying the boiling fruit. Three expert tasters had orders to report progress every half hour.

Then she ordered two hundred great kneading troughs. The pastry cooks rolled up their sleeves and began to knead the dough with cries of "Hi! Hi!" that could be heard for miles.

When each troughful of paste was approved it was moulded with care into the form of bricks, and with the aid of the engineer-in-chief, the majestic edifice was begun. The inside of the monument was divided into as many compartments as there were kinds of fruit.

Nothing was needed then but to crown the delicious edifice by placing upon it the crust—that is, the roof, or dome. This delicate operation was entrusted to the engineer-in-chief who now showed his superior genius. The dome, made beforehand of a single piece, was raised in the air by means of twelve balloons. First it was directed by ropes exactly over the top of the tart; then at the word of command it gently descended upon the right spot. It was not a quarter of an inch out of place.

But all was not over. How should this colossal tart be cooked? That was the question that puzzled all the people of the Greedy country, who came in crowds—to gaze at the wonderful spectacle.

Mother Mitchel, smiling at the general bewilderment, mounted the summit of the tart; she waved her crutch in the air, and while her cat miaowed in his sweetest voice, suddenly there issued from the woods a vast number of masons, drawing wagons of well-baked bricks, which they had prepared in secret.

In two days an enormous furnace was built around and above the colossal tart, which found itself shut up in an immense earthen pot. When the fire was lighted in the ovens, and they saw the clouds of smoke rolling above the dome that announced that the cooking had begun, the joy of the people was boundless.

After two days the tart was cooked to perfection. The whole country was perfumed with its delicious aroma. Nothing more remained but to take down the furnaces. Mother Mitchel made her official announcement to His Majesty, who was delighted, and complimented her upon her punctuality. One day was still wanting to complete the month.

The TART, unveiled, appeared at last in all its majesty and splendor. The wildest excitement and rapture ran through the land of the Greedy. Each one sniffed the appetizing perfume with open nostrils. Then the people of town and country, joined hands and danced in a ring around the grand confection.

No one dared to touch the tart before the arrival of His Majesty. Meanwhile, something must be done to quiet the universal impatience, and they resolved to show Mother Mitchel the gratitude with which all hearts were filled. She was crowned with the laurel of *conquerors*. Then they placed her, with her crutch and her cat, upon a sort of throne, and carried her all around her vast work.

The royal procession arrived. A grand stairway had been built, so that the king and his ministers could mount to the summit of this monumental tart. The king thus addressed his people,

"My children," said he, "you adore tarts. You despise all other food. If you could, you would even eat tarts in your sleep. Very well. Eat as much as you like. Here is one big enough to satisfy you. But know this, that while there remains a single crumb of this tart, all other food is forbidden you on pain of death. While you are here, I have ordered all the pantries to be emptied, and all the butchers, bakers, pork and milk dealers, to shut up their shops. Why leave them open? Why indeed? Have you not here what you love best, and enough to last you ever, *ever* so long? Devote yourselves to it with all your hearts. I do not wish you to be bored with the sight of any other food.

"Greedy ones! behold your TART!"

What enthusiastic applause, what frantic hurrahs rent the air, in answer to this eloquent speech from the throne!

"Long live the king, Mother Mitchel, and her cat! Long live the tart! Down with soup! Down with bread! To the bottom of the sea with all beefsteaks, mutton chops and roasts!"

At last, the signal was given. The king smiled at the opening in the tart; though vast, it hardly showed more than a mouse hole in the monstrous wall.

Who can tell how long the feast would have lasted if the king had not given his command that it should cease? Once more they expressed their gratitude with cries so

249

stifled that they resembled grunts, and then rushed to the river. Never had a nation been so besmeared. Some were daubed to the eyes, others had their ears and hair all sticky. As for the little ones, they were marmalade from head to foot.

Before returning home, the people presented themselves before the king to receive his commands.

"Children!" said he, "the feast will begin again exactly at six o'clock. You shall feast twice a day as long as the tart lasts. Do not forget! Yes! if there is not enough in this one, I will even order ANOTHER from Mother Mitchel. Your happiness is my only aim. You understand? Noon, and six o'clock! There is no need for me to say be punctual! Go, then, my children—be happy!"

The second feast was as gay as the first, and as long. But the king fancied that the breach made in the tart was a little smaller than that of the morning.

" 'Tis well!" said he, " 'tis well! Wait till tomorrow, my friends; yes, till day after tomorrow, and *next week*!"

The next day the feast still went on gayly; yet at the evening meal the king noticed some empty seats.

"Why is this?" said he, with pretended indifference, to the court physician.

"Your Majesty," said the physician, "a few weak stomachs, that is all."

On the next day there were larger empty spaces. The enthusiasm visibly abated. The eighth day the crowd had diminished one half; and each day grew less until on the eleventh day only one hundred remained, and on the twelfth —alas! who would have thought it?—a single one answered to the call. He was known in the town by the name of Patapouf. They dug out a fresh lump for him from the middle of the tart. It quickly vanished and he retired with great dignity, proud to maintain the honor of his name and the glory of the Greedy Kingdom.

But the next day, even he, the very last, appeared no more. The unfortunate Patapouf had succumbed, and, like all the other inhabitants of the country, was in a very bad way. In short, it was soon known that the whole town had suffered agonies that night from too much tart. Mother Mitchel was in despair. All the city was one vast hospital. No one was seen in the streets but doctors, running from house to house in frantic haste. It was dreadful! As for the king, he held his tongue and shut himself up in his palace, but a secret joy shone in his eyes. He waited three days without a word.

The third day, the king said to his ministers,

"Let us go now and see how my poor people are doing, and feel their pulse a little."

The good king went to every house, without forgetting a single one. He visited small and great, rich and poor.

"Oh, oh! Your Majesty," said all, "the tart was good, but may we never see it again! Plague on that tart! Better were dry bread. Oh, a morsel of dry bread, how good it would be!"

"No, indeed," replied the king. *There is more of that tart!*"

"What! Your Majesty, *must* we eat it all?"

"You *must*!" sternly replied the king; "you MUST! By the immortal beefsteaks! not one of you shall have a slice of bread, and not a loaf shall be baked in the kingdom while there remains a crumb of that excellent tart!"

"What misery!" thought these poor people. "That tart forever."

The sufferers were in despair. There was only one cry through all the town: "Ow! ow! ow!" For even the strongest and most courageous were in horrible agonies. They twisted, they lay down, they got up. The dogs were no happier than their masters; even they had had too much tart.

In the midst of this terrible consternation the king remained relentless during eight days. His heart bled for his people, but the lesson must sink deep if it was to bear fruit in the future. When their pains were cured, little by little, through fasting alone, and his subjects pronounced these trembling words, "We are hungry!" the king sent them trays laden with—the inevitable tart.

"Ah!" cried they, with anguish, "the tart again! Always the tart, and nothing but the tart! Better were death!"

A few, who were almost famished, shut their eyes, and tried to eat a bit of the detested food; but it was all in vain —they could not swallow a mouthful.

At length came the happy day when the king, thinking their punishment had been severe enough and could never be forgotten, believed them at length cured of their greediness. That day he ordered Mother Mitchel to make a superexcellent soup of which a bowl was sent to every family.

The next day, more soup. This time the king allowed slices of bread in it. How this good soup comforted all the town! The next day there was a little more bread in it and a little soup meat. Then for a few days the kind king gave them roast beef and vegetables. The cure was complete.

The joy over this new diet was as great as ever had been felt for the tart. It promised to last longer.

The Greedy people never fell back into their old ways. Their once puffed-out, sallow faces now shone with health. The butchers and bakers reopened their shops; the pastry cooks and confectioners shut theirs. The country of the Greedy was turned upside down, and if it kept its name, it was only from habit. As for the tart, it was forgotten. Today, in that marvellous country, there cannot be found a paper of sugarplums or a basket of cakes. If they still have a king, he may well be proud to be their ruler.

Ask no more about Mother Mitchel. She was ridiculed without measure by those who had adored her. To complete her misfortune, she lost her cat. Alas for Mother Mitchel!

The king received the reward of his wisdom. His grateful people called him neither Charles the Bold, nor Peter the Terrible, nor Louis the Great, but always by the noble name of Prosper I, the Reasonable.

Mistress Esteem Elliott's Molasses Cake

Adapted from the story by Kate Upson Clark.
Wideawake, November 1891.   15 minutes

"Obed!" called Mistress Achsah Ely from her front porch, "step over to Squire Belding's, quick! Here's a tea-cup! Ask Mistress Belding for the loan of some molasses. Nothing but molasses and hot water helps the baby when he is having such a turn of colic. Make haste, Obed!"

At that very moment Squire Belding's little daughter Hitty was travelling toward Mistress Ely's for the purpose of borrowing molasses to sweeten a ginger cake. Hitty and Obed, who were of an age, met, compared notes, and then returned to their respective homes. Shortly afterward both of them darted forth again, bound on the same errand as before, only in different directions.

Mr. Chapin, the storekeeper, hadn't "set eyes on any molasses for a week. The river's frozen over so mean and solid," he said, "there's no knowing when there'll be any molasses in town."

There had been very peculiar weather in Colchester during this month of October 1705. First, on the 13th, a very early date, had come a "terrible cold snap," lasting three days. This was followed by two days of unusual mildness. The river had frozen over during the "cold snap," and the ice had melted during the warm days, until, on the 19th, it was breaking up and preparing to go out to sea. In the night of the 19th had come a frigid blast, colder than the original one. After the cold wind there was a heavy snow-storm. All Colchester lay under three feet of snow. Footpaths and roads were broken out somewhat in the immediate village, but no farther. It was most unusual to have the river closed so early in the season, and consequently the winter supplies, which were secured from New London and Norwich, had not been laid in. Even Mr. Chapin, the store-keeper, was but poorly supplied with staples of which he ordinarily kept an abundance on hand.

So when Obed and Hitty had made the tour of the neighborhood, they found but one family, that of Deacon Esteem Elliott, the richest man in the place, which had any molasses. Mistress Elliott, in spite of her wealth, was said to be "none too free with her stuff," and she did not want to lend any molasses under the circumstances, for "a trifling foolish" cake. Obed's representation of the distress of the Ely baby, however, appealed even to her, and she lent him a large spoonful of the precious liquid.

That afternoon there was as much visiting about among the Colchester housewives as the drifts permitted. Such a state of things had never been known since the town was settled. No molasses! And Thanksgiving appointed for the first Thursday in November! Pray what would Thanks-giving amount to, they inquired, with no pumpkin pies, no baked beans, no molasses cake.

Mistress Esteem Elliott was even more troubled than the rest of Colchester, for was not her buxom daughter, and only child, Prudence Ann, to be married on Thanks-giving Day to the son of a great magnate in the neighboring town of Hebron? And was it not the intention to invite all of the aristocracy of both towns to be present at the mar-riage feast?

Mistress Elliott accordingly made her way upon this Tuesday afternoon, October 19, 1705, over to Mistress Achsah Ely's. There she found Mistress Belding, who, re-membering Mistress Elliott's refusal to lend her molasses, was naturally somewhat chill in her manner.

Mistress Elliott had scarcely pulled off her homespun leggings (made with stout and ample feet) and pulled out her knitting work, when Mistress Camberly, the parson's wife, came in.

"And what are we going to do, Mistress Ely?" she burst out, as soon as the door was opened at her knock. "Not a drop of molasses to be had for love nor money, and Thanksgiving Day set for the 4th of November!"

"Mistress Elliott has a-plenty of molasses," said Mistress Belding.

"I'd have you know, Mistress Betty Belding," retorted Mistress Elliott, "that I have a bare quart or so in my jug, and, so far as I can learn, that is all that the whole town of Colchester has got to depend upon till the roads or the river can be broken to Norwich."

Mistress Ely well understood this little passage-at-arms, for Obed had told her the whole story; but as her baby had been cured by Mistress Elliott's molasses, she did not think it proper to interfere in the matter. Neither did the good parson's wife, although she could not understand the rights of the case. She simply repeated her first question: "What are we going to do about it, I should like to know?"

"I wonder if Thanksgviing Day could not be put off a week," suggested Mistress Belding, who had a good head, and was even reported to give such good advice to her husband that he always thought best to heed it.

"Such a thing was never heard of!" cried Mistress Elliott.

"But there's no law against it," insisted Mistress Belding boldly. "By a week from the set day there will surely be some means of getting about the country, and then we can have a Thanksgiving that's worth the setting down to."

After a long talk the good women separated in some doubt, but as Squire Belding and Mr. Ely were two of the three selectmen, they were soon acquainted with the drift of the afternoon's discussion. The result of it all is thus chronicled in the town records of Colchester:

"At a legal town-meeting held in Colchester, October 29, 1705, it was voted that WHEREAS there was a Thanksgiving appointed to be held on the first Thursday in November, and our present circumstances being such that it cannot with convenience be attended on that day, it is therefore voted and agreed by the inhabitants as aforesaid (concluding the thing will not be otherwise than well resented) that the second Thursday of November aforesaid shall be set aside for that service."

This proceeding was, on the whole, as the selectmen had hoped that it would be, "well resented" among the Colchester people, but there was one household in which there was rebellion. In the great sanded kitchen of Deacon Esteem Elliott, pretty, spoilt Prudence Ann was fairly raging over it.

"I had set my heart on being married on Thanksgiving Day," she sobbed. "And here it won't be Thanksgiving Day at all! And as for putting off a wedding, everybody knows there is no surer way of bringing ill luck down than that! I say I won't have it put off! But we can't have any party with no molasses in town! Oh, dear! I might as well be married in the back kitchen with a linsey gown on, as if I were the daughter of old Betty, the pie woman! There!"

Then the proud girl would break into fresh sobs, and vow vengeance upon the selectmen of Colchester. She even sent her father to argue with them, but it was of no use. They had known all along that the Elliotts did not want the festival day put off, but nobody in Colchester minded very much if the Elliotts were a little crossed.

Prudence Ann would not face the reality till after the Sabbath was past. On that day the expectant bridegroom managed to break his way through the drifts from Hebron, and he was truly grieved, as he should have been, at the very unhappy state of mind of his betrothed. He avowed himself, however, ready to do just what Prudence Ann and her family decided was best.

On Monday morning Mistress Elliott sat down with her unreasonable daughter and had a serious talk with her.

"Now, Prudence Ann," she began, "you must give up crying and fretting. If you are going to be married on Thursday, we have got a great deal of work to do between now and then. If you are going to wait till next week, I want to know it. Of course you can't have a large party, if you choose to be married on the 4th, but we will ask John's folks and Aunt Susanna and Uncle Martin and Parson Camberley and his wife. We can bake enough for them with what's in the house. If you wait another week, you can probably have a better party—and now you have it all in a nutshell."

Prudence Ann was hysterical even yet, but at last her terror of a postponed wedding overcame every other consideration. The day was set for the 4th, and the few guests were bidden accordingly.

On the morning of the wedding, on a neat shelf in the back kitchen of the Elliott residence, various delicacies were resting, which had been baked for the banquet. Mistress Elliott's molasses had been enough to make a vast cake and several pumpkin pies. These, hot from the oven, had been placed in the coolness of the back kitchen until they should be ready for eating.

It so happened that Miss Hitty Belding's sharp eyes, as she passed Mistress Elliott's back door, bound on an errand to the house of the neighbor living just beyond, fell upon the rich golden brown of this wonderful cake. As such tempting dainties were rare in Colchester at just this time, it is not strange that her childish soul coveted it, for Hitty was but ten years old. As she walked on she met Obed Ely.

"I tell you what, Obed," said Miss Hitty, "you ought to see the great molasses cake which Mistress Elliott has made for Prudence Ann's wedding. It is in her back kitchen. I saw it right by the door. She wouldn't lend my mother any molasses to make us a cake. I wish I had hers!"

"So do I!" rejoined Obed, with watering lips. "I'm going to peek in and see it."

Obed went and "peeked," while Hitty sauntered slowly on. The sight of the cake under the circumstances was too much for even so well-brought-up a boy as Obed. Without stopping to really think what he was doing, he unwound from his neck his great woollen "comforter," wrapped it hastily around the cake, and was walking with it beside Hitty in the lonely, drifted country road five minutes later. The hearts of the two little conspirators — for they felt guilty enough — beat very hard, but they could not help thinking how good that cake would taste. A certain Good-sir Canty's cornhouse stood near them in a clump of trees beside the road, and as the door was open they crept in, gulped down great "chunks" of cake, distributed vast slices of what was left about their persons, Obed taking by far the lion's share, and then they parted, vowing eternal secrecy. Nobody had seen them, and something which happened just after they had left Mistress Elliott's back kitchen directed suspicion to an entirely different quarter.

Not two minutes after Obed's "comforter" had been thrown around the great cake a beautiful calf, the pride of Mistress Elliott's heart, which was usually kept tied in the barn just beyond the back kitchen, somehow unfastened her rope and came strolling along just past the open back door. The odor of the pumpkin pies naturally interested her, and she proceeded to lick up the delicious creamy filling of one after another with great zest.

Just as she was finishing the very last one of the four or five which had stood there, Mistress Elliott appeared upon the scene, to find her precious dainties gone, leaving behind them only a few broken bits of pie crust. A series of "short, sharp shocks" then rent the air, summoning Prudence Ann and Delcy, the maid, to the scene of the calamity.

259

In a very short time Prudence Ann lay upon the sitting-room lounge passing from one fainting fit into another, and Delcy was out in search of the doctor and such family friends as were likely to be of services in this unexpected dilemma. It was, of course, supposed that the calf had devoured the whole of the mighty cake as well as the pies. It was lucky for Obed and Hitty that the poor beast could not speak. As it was, nobody so much as thought of accusing them of the theft, though there were plenty of crumbs in their pockets, while the death of the innocent heifer was loudly demanded by the angry Prudence Ann. It was only by diplomacy that Mistress Elliott was able to preserve the life of her favorite, which, if it had really eaten the cake, must surely have perished.

The wedding finally came off on the 4th, and nuts, apples, and cider were said to be the chief refreshments. Prudence Ann, however, probably secured the "good luck" for which she was so anxious, for there is no record nor tradition to the contrary in all Colchester.

Nothing would probably ever have been known of the real fate of the famous cake if the tale had not been told by Mistress Hitty in her old age to her grandchildren, with appropriate warnings to them never to commit similar misdemeanors themselves.

The Pumpkin Giant

Adapted from *The Pot of Gold* by Mary E. Wilkins Freeman.   13 minutes

A very long time ago, there were no pumpkins; people had never eaten a pumpkin pie, or even stewed pumpkin; and that was the time when the Pumpkin Giant flourished.

There have been a great many giants since the world began, and although a select few of them have been good giants, the majority of them have been bad. But the Pumpkin Giant was an uncommonly bad one, and his general appearance and his behavior were such as to make one shudder. He was very tall; he probably would have over-topped most of the giants you have ever heard of. The Pumpkin Giant had a very large yellow head, which was also smooth and shiny. His eyes were big and round, and glowed like coals of fire. His mouth, which stretched half around his head, was furnished with rows of pointed teeth, and he was never known to hold it any other way than wide open.

The giant's castle was situated on a mountain, as it ought to have been, and there was also the usual courtyard before it, and the customary moat, which was full of— bones!

The Pumpkin Giant was fonder of little boys and girls than anything else in the world; but he was somewhat fonder of little boys, and more particularly of fat little boys.

The fear and horror of this giant extended over the whole country. There was good reason why the king shook: his only daughter, the Princess Ariadne Diana, was probably the fattest princess in the whole world at that date.

She was never allowed to leave the palace without a body-guard of fifty knights. Meanwhile amongst the ordinary people the ravages of the Pumpkin Giant were frightful. It was apprehended at one time that there would be very few fat little girls, and no fat little boys at all, left in the kingdom.

And what made matters worse, at that time the giant commenced taking a tonic to increase his appetite.

Finally the king, in desperation, issued a proclamation that he would knight anyone, be he noble or common, who would cut off the head of the Pumpkin Giant. This was the king's usual method of rewarding any noble deed in his kingdom. It was a cheap method, and besides everybody liked to be a knight.

When the king issued his proclamation every man in the kingdom who was not already a knight, straightway tried to contrive ways and means to kill the Pumpkin Giant.

There was one man who lived not far from the terrible giant's castle, a poor man, his only worldly wealth consisting of a large potato field and a cottage in front of it. But he had a boy of twelve, an only son, who rivaled the Princess Ariadne Diana in point of fatness. The fat boy's name was Aeneas, his father's name was Patroclus, and his mother's Daphne.

One morning Patroclus and Aeneas were out in the field digging potatoes, for new potatoes were just in the market. All at once the earth trembled violently. Patroclus and Aeneas looked up and saw the Pumpkin Giant coming with his mouth wide open. "Get behind me, oh, my darling son!" cried Patroclus.

Aeneas obeyed, but it was of no use; for you could see his cheeks each side of his father's waistcoat.

The Pumpkin Giant strode along faster and faster, opening his mouth wider and wider, until they could fairly hear it crack at the corners.

Then Patroclus picked up an enormous Young Planta-genet potato and threw it plump into the Pumpkin Giant's mouth. The giant choked and gasped, and choked and gasped, and finally tumbled down and died.

Patroclus and Aeneas, while the giant was choking, had run to the house and locked themselves in; then they looked out of the kitchen window. When they saw the giant tumble down and lie quite still, they knew he must be dead. Then Daphne was immediately cured of the Giant's Shakes, and got out of bed for the first time in two years. Patroclus sharpened the carving knife on the kitchen stove, and they all went out to the potato field.

They cautiously approached the prostrate giant, for fear he might be shamming, and might suddenly spring up at them and—Aeneas. But no, he did not move at all; he was quite dead. And, all taking turns, they hacked off his head with the carving knife.

The king was notified of the death of the Pumpkin Giant, and was greatly rejoiced. But though his gratitude for the noble deed knew no bounds, he omitted to give the promised reward and knight Patroclus.

Next spring running vines grew all over Patroclus's potato field, and in the fall giants' heads. There they were all over the field, hundreds of them! Then there was con-sternation indeed!

"There was one Pumpkin Giant before," said they, "now there will be a whole army of them. If it was dreadful then, what will it be in the future? But when some time had elapsed and nothing more of the giants appeared above the surface of the potato field, the people began to feel a little easier.

Now Aeneas had been born with a desire to put every-thing into his mouth to taste it. This propensity was so alarming in his babyhood that Daphne purchased a book of antidotes, and there was scarcely one which had not been resorted to from time to time.

Aeneas had become acquainted with the peculiar flavor of almost everything in his immediate vicinity except the giant's heads; and he naturally enough cast longing eyes at them. Night and day he wondered what a giant's head would taste like, till finally one day when Patroclus was away he stole out into the potato field, cut a bit out of one of the giants' heads, and ate it. He was almost afraid to, but he reflected that his mother could give him an antidote, so he ventured. It tasted very sweet and nice. He liked it so much that he cut off another piece and ate that, then another and another, until he had eaten two thirds of a giant's head. Then he thought it was about time for him to go in and tell his mother and take an antidote, though he did not feel ill at all yet.

"Mother," said he, rolling slowing into the cottage, "I have eaten two thirds of a giant's head, and I guess you had better give me an antidote."

"Oh, my precious son!" groaned Daphne. "How could you?" She looked in her book of antidotes, but could not find one antidote for a giant's head.

"Oh, Aeneas, my dear, dear son!" cried Daphne, "There is no antidote for a giant's head! What shall we do?"

Then she sat down and wept, and Aeneas wept too, as loud as he possibly could. All day his mother and father sat weeping and watching Aeneas, expecting every moment to see him die. But he did not die; on the contrary he had never felt so well in his life.

Finally at sunset Aeneas looked up and laughed. "I am not going to die," said he; "I never felt so well; you had better stop crying. And I am going out to get some more of that giant's head; I am hungry." "Don't, don't," cried his father and mother; but he would go. He came back with a whole giant's head in his arms.

"See here, father and mother," he cried. "We'll all have some of this; it evidently is not poison, and it is good— a great deal better than potatoes!"

Patroclus and Daphne hesitated, but they were hungry, too.

"It is good," said Daphne; "but I think it would be better cooked." So she put some in a kettle of water over the fire and let it boil awhile. Then she dished it up, and they all ate it. It was delicious. It tasted more like stewed pumpkin than anything else; in fact, it was stewed pumpkin.

Daphne was inventive, and something of a genius; and next day she concocted another dish out of the giants' heads. She boiled them, and sifted them, and mixed them with eggs and sugar and milk and spice; then she lined some plates with puff paste, filled them with the mixture and set them in the oven to bake.

The result was unparalleled; nothing half so exquisite had ever been tasted. They were all in ecstasies, Aeneas in particular. They gathered all the giants' heads and stored them in the cellar and Daphne baked pies every day.

One morning the king had been out hunting, and happened to ride by the cottage of Patroclus with a train of his knights. Daphne was baking pies as usual, and the kitchen door and window were both open, so the delicious odor of the pies perfumed the whole air about the cottage.

"What is it smells so utterly lovely?" exclaimed the king, sniffing in rapture, and sent a page in to see.

"The housewife is baking giant's head pies," said the page, returning.

"What?" thundered the king. "Bring one out to me!"

So the page brought out a pie to him, and after all his knights had tasted to be sure it was not poison, and the king watched them sharply for a few moments to be sure they were not killed, he tasted too.

Then he beamed. It was a new sensation, and a new sensation is a great boon to a king.

"I never tasted anything so altogether superfine, so utterly magnificent, in my life," cried the king. "Stewed peacocks' tongues from the Baltic are not to be compared with it! Call out the housewife immediately!"

So Daphne came out trembling, and Patroclus and Aeneas also.

"What a charming lad!" exclaimed the king as his glance fell upon Aeneas. "Now tell me about these wonderful pies, and I will reward you as becomes a monarch!"

Then Patroclus fell on his knees and related the whole history of the giant's head pies from the beginning.

The king actually blushed. "And I forgot to knight you, oh, noble and brave man, and to make a lady of your admirable wife!"

Then the king leaned gracefully down from his saddle and struck Patroclus with his jeweled sword and knighted him on the spot.

The whole family went to live at the royal palace. The roses in the royal garden were uprooted, and giants' heads (or pumpkins, as they came to be called) were sown in their stead; all the royal parks also were turned into pumpkin fields.

Patroclus was in constant attendance on the king, and used to stand all day in his antechamber. Daphne had a position of great responsibility, for she superintended the baking of the pumpkin pies, and Aeneas finally married the Princess Ariadne Diana.

They were wedded in great state by fifty archbishops, and all the newspapers united in stating that they were the most charming and well matched young couple that had ever been united in the kingdom.

The stone entrance of the Pumpkin Giant's castle was securely fastened, and upon it was engraved an inscription composed by the first poet of the kingdom, for which the king made him laureate, and gave him the liberal pension of fifty pumpkin pies per year.

266

The following is the inscription in full:

> Here dwelt the Pumpkin Giant once,
>   He's dead the nation doth rejoice,
> For, while he was alive, he lived
>   by e - - - - g dear, fat, little boys.

The inscription is said to remain to this day; if you were to go there you would probably see it.